BIOL 1103L

CONCEPTS OF
BIOLOGY

LABORATORY MANUAL · SIXTH EDITION

DIVISION OF BIOLOGICAL SCIENCES · UNIVERSITY OF GEORGIA

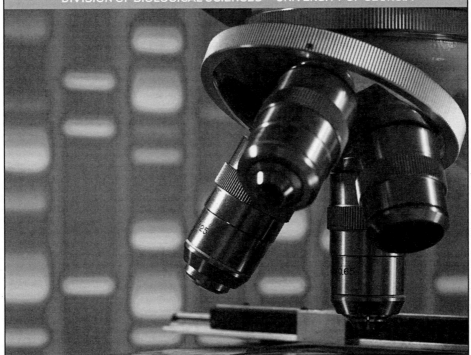

CONTRIBUTING AUTHORS: NORRIS ARMSTRONG, MARGUERITE BRICKMAN,
CARA GORMALLY, A. KELLY LANE, KRISTEN MILLER

CONTRIBUTING EDITOR: KIMBERLY A. BROWN

DIVISION OF BIOLOGICAL SCIENCES
THE UNIVERSITY OF GEORGIA
ATHENS, GA

D1411638

bluedoor

flexible & affordable learning solutions™

Chief Executive Officer: Jon K. Earl

President, College: Lucas Tomasso
President, Private Sector: Dawn Earl

Print Solutions Manager: Connie Dayton
Digital Solutions Manager: Amber Wahl
Content Solutions Manager: Anne Loyle-Langholz
Developmental & Production Coordinator: Meg Olstad
Senior Project Coordinator: Dan Woods
Senior Project Coordinator: Peggy Li
Project Coordinator: Erica Nilsen
Project Coordinator: Kelli Fleck
Project Coordinator: Andy Neidt
Project Coordinator: Kristin Johnson
Production Assistant: Stephanie Larson
Production Assistant: Jessie Steigauf

Cover Design: Erica Nilsen

ISBN-13: 978-1-68135-593-1

© 2017 by The University of Georgia Research Foundation, Inc. and bluedoor, LLC.

© Cover images by Shutterstock.

Published by bluedoor, LLC
              10949 Bren Road East
              Minneapolis, MN 55343-9613
              800-979-1624
              www.bluedoorpublishing.com

All rights reserved. Making copies of any part of this book for any purpose other than your own personal use is a violation of the United States Copyright laws. No part of this book may be used or reproduced in any form or by any means, or stored in a database retrieval system, without prior written permission of bluedoor, LLC.

Printed in the United States of America.
10 9 8 7 6 5 4 3 2 1

ACKNOWLEDGEMENTS

This work was developed under sponsorship by the US National Science Foundation through award number 0511307 for the project titled "Promoting Inquiry and Scientific Literacy in Non-Science Major Undergraduate Biology".

The authors gratefully acknowledge the feedback, ideas, and creativity of BIOL 1103L Laboratory Managers and Graduate Laboratory Assistants that helped produce this edition. We especially thank A. Kelly Lane, Department of Genetics, and Dr. Joey LaMattina, Department of Biochemistry, for their outstanding additions to lab activities and logistics, student assessment, and instructional materials.

TABLE OF CONTENTS

ADMINISTRATIVE ITEMS

Your GLA's Name: _____

Office Location: _____

Phone: _____

E-mail Address: _____

General Academic Rules

DO I NEED TO SHOW UP FOR LAB?

Attendance is required for this class. Missing even one class means that you have missed a significant portion of the course. If you arrive for lab more than 10 minutes late or leave the lab early without your instructor's permission, you will be marked as absent. Each lab that is missed without a valid excuse will result in an automatic point deduction from your final lab score. Students who miss **FOUR** or more labs *either with or without valid excuses* at the end of the semester will not receive credit for the course.

WHAT DO I DO IF I MISS A LAB?

If you know in **advance** that you will miss a lab, and you have a valid excuse, you must contact your lab teaching assistant (GLA) **before** the lab for reassignment to another lab period. If you don't know in advance that you will miss lab, but have a valid excuse, you will be allowed to make up the lab provided you contact your lab instructor within 48 hours of the absence. A valid excuse is one that is written, verifiable, and covers the date and time of your scheduled lab class. Oversleeping, job conflicts, hangovers, and "just not into it today" do not constitute acceptable excuses.

Students who have missed four or more labs due to extenuating circumstances and wish to avoid a failing grade should withdraw from the course or request an Incomplete. After the midpoint in the semester, permission to withdraw must be obtained from the Office of the Vice President for Student Affairs.

WHAT KIND OF WORK SHOULD I EXPECT TO DO FOR LAB?

You will be required to complete formal (assigned grade) and informal (completed acceptably) assignments for almost every class. Some of these assignments you will complete in class while others will require you to work outside of class.

Assignments are due in class on the days indicated in your syllabus or as otherwise specified by your instructor. If you show up to lab without a completed assignment, you will automatically lose 10% of the assignment's total points for every day it is late (i.e., if your assignment is worth 20 points, every day it is late will result in a deduction of 2 points). **Exception: Pre-lab assignments not completed by the stated due date will not be given any credit.**

WHAT HAPPENS IF I MISSED AN ASSIGNMENT FOR A VALID REASON?

For those students who have a **valid** excuse, make-up assignments are due within one week of the missed lab and may include any or all of the following: completing the lab with a different section; submitting all homework, quizzes, or any other assignment associated with the missed lab. Students who fail to complete the make-up work within the allocated time will not receive credit for the lab exercise. See your lab instructor for specific instructions regarding the make-up assignment for a particular lab.

EXPECTATIONS ABOUT GROUP WORK AND PLAGIARISM

Just as scientists regularly share ideas, compare notes, and give each other constructive feedback, you are *encouraged* to interact with your GLA and your classmates when completing your in-class work and your homework. However, **you are expected to complete all written assignments by yourself** unless otherwise directed by your GLA. Using another person's written work, referred to as "copying" or "plagiarism," is defined in the University of Georgia's academic honesty policy, *Culture of Honesty*, as "Submission for academic advancement the words, ideas, opinions or theories of another that are not common knowledge, without appropriate attribution to that other person." This is the case **no matter how small the assignment**. This policy can be found online; it provides you with a non-exhaustive list of types of plagiarism. **You acknowledged and signed this document when you first enrolled at UGA and are therefore committed to this policy. You are expected to be familiar with it.**

In regards to group work, Academic Dishonesty may also occur in the form of "Unauthorized Assistance." This can include "submitting a group assignment, or allowing that assignment to be submitted, representing that the project is the work of all of the members of the group when less than all of the group members assisted substantially in its preparation" (*Culture of Honesty*, 2007).

In other words, it is okay if you confer with your GLA or other students on how to set up an experiment or interpret results and then use **what you have learned** from the conversation as a basis for writing up an assignment. It is **not** okay to simply copy what someone else has written or tells you to write or to do less than your fair share of the work in a group assignment. Possible honor code violations will be reported to the Office of the Vice President for Instruction for an academic hearing.

→ **If you ever have a question about whether or not you have crossed the fine line between group work and independent work, ask your GLA for assistance *before* you hand in an assignment.**

Do I Have to Clean Up after Myself?

The laboratory rooms are used by several classes each day—in fact, in the course of the week, nearly 600 students will use the BIOL 1103 labs and equipment. Part of being a member of the university community is good citizenship and consideration for fellow students. Please do your part to leave the lab clean and orderly. Any equipment you use should be returned to the place where you found it. Ask if you're not sure where something belongs. Report any broken equipment to your GLA **immediately**.

General Lab Rules

- All students must adhere to the dress code for this lab course. This means your toes to your waist must be covered at all times. Failure to follow dress code will result in you being dismissed from the lab and accruing an absence.

- All tools, test tubes, etc., must be washed, dried, and returned to the appropriate place (not left by the sink). Glassware should be rinsed off before being returned to its appropriate place.

- Waste paper and other debris must be collected and disposed of properly.

- Please be careful not to contaminate any reagents in use in the lab. You wouldn't want your experiment ruined because someone from an earlier lab was sloppy; try not to ruin things up for students in later labs.

- Wipe off your bench at the end of the lab period.

- Turn off microscope lights whenever not in use.

- Microscope slides: Flat slides and coverslips **must** be discarded in the broken glass bins. Do not throw away pre-prepared slides (slides bought from a company or prepared by your instructor) or depression slides (thicker than regular slides and with a concave depression in the surface).

- When your GLA indicates to do so, please dispose of biologically hazardous waste in the appropriate container, not in the regular trash bin.

SAFETY REGULATIONS

So far in the history of this lab, we have not lost any students (or pieces of them). We would like to keep it that way. Therefore, we must insist on a few safety rules. If your GLA feels that your behavior is inappropriate or unsafe, they have the right to ask you to leave the laboratory. In such instances you will not receive credit for the lab.

- **No eating, drinking, or smoking in the lab.** (We know that smoking tends to kill slowly. However, it can do so much more quickly and dramatically in the presence of flammable liquids and gases.)

- **Safety goggles are recommended while working in the lab and may be required for certain lab exercises.** Contact lenses *are not recommended* for labs in which caustic and/or volatile chemicals will be used.

- **Plastic gloves should be used during lab exercises in which chemicals will be used or as otherwise directed by your GLA.** All cuts should be bandaged.

- **Long hair should be secured away from the face and shoulders during lab periods in which an open flame is present.**

- **Accidents and/or injuries (cuts, spills, bites, etc.) should be attended to and washed *immediately*.** If you experience ANY kind of accident or injury, let your GLA know immediately. A first aid kit is available in your lab room.

- **Chemical wastes should *only* be disposed of according to the directions given by your instructor.** (Do *NOT* pour them down the sink.) If it is unclear how to dispose of a solution, ask your instructor.

- **Hands should be washed before leaving lab, particularly on weeks when working with living organisms.** (You don't want to bring any uninvited friends home with you.)

- **Safety showers are outside the lab classrooms. Eyewashes are available at sinks in the lab classrooms.** Use cold water when using the eyewash. Also note the location of the lab's fire extinguisher and broken glass containers. Your GLA will explain how and when to use all equipment.

- *Dress Code:* **Toes to waist must be completely covered at all times when you are in lab. No exceptions.** During the water quality lab, it is recommended that you wear old clothes.

ETHICAL CONTRACT

ETHICAL CONTRACT FOR STUDENTS PARTICIPATING IN A COOPERATIVE, INQUIRY CLASSROOM

Students—Please read, sign, and turn in this page during the second week laboratory class meets. The next page contains a copy that you are to keep for your reference.

Learning in a cooperative environment with inquiry-based activities should be stimulating, demanding, and fair, but this approach is different from the competitive classroom structure with traditional, verification-type activities. Therefore, it is important for us to be clear about mutual expectations. Below is the code of conduct that is expected of students in this class. This code is intended to maximize thinking, reflection, debate, and exchange of ideas in an atmosphere of mutual respect while preserving individual ownership of written words. If you feel you do not understand or cannot agree to these expectations, there will be an opportunity to discuss this with your instructor and classmates in the first laboratory class.

1. I will work cooperatively with my classmates, both by listening and giving thought to others' ideas, as well as contributing my own ideas. I will do my share of the work as I expect others to do their share.

2. I understand that using one's own words when writing promotes understanding and learning. I will regularly record my ideas and questions in my own words during lab.

3. I understand that giving concise and accurate oral presentations is a useful skill to have. I will take advantage of the opportunities in this class to develop that skill.

4. I expect to share data with my team members. With the exception of shared data, I will write assignments by myself, using my own words. I will prepare my own graphs, figures, or charts and do my own interpretations, and will not represent others' work as my own, even during group projects or presentations.

5. I will abide by The University of Georgia's Academic Honesty standards as outlined in *A Culture of Honesty*. It is my responsibility to familiarize myself with the current UGA academic honesty policies as they apply to BIOL 1103L.

NOTICE OF PARTICIPATION IN A MANDATORY COURSE FIELD TRIP

6. I hereby acknowledge my awareness that my participation in the BIOL 1103L field trip to test water quality may expose me to risk of property damage and bodily or personal injury that may prove fatal. Examples of risks that I may be exposed to include: traffic accidents, falls, drowning, insect bites, stings, snake bites, poison ivy, water-borne pathogens, etc., as well as other risks that may not be foreseeable. I hereby assume any and all such risks.

I hereby certify that I am at least 18 years of age and that I have read and understand and agree to abide by the guidelines described in this Biology 1103 laboratory manual.

_____

Signed   *Date*

ETHICAL CONTRACT

ETHICAL CONTRACT FOR STUDENTS PARTICIPATING IN A COOPERATIVE, INQUIRY CLASSROOM

Student copy: Keep for your reference.

Learning in a cooperative environment with inquiry-based activities should be stimulating, demanding, and fair, but this approach is different from the competitive classroom structure with traditional, verification-type activities. Therefore, it is important for us to be clear about mutual expectations. Below is the code of conduct that is expected of students in this class. This code is intended to maximize thinking, reflection, debate, and exchange of ideas in an atmosphere of mutual respect while preserving individual ownership of written words. If you feel you do not understand or cannot agree to these expectations, there will be an opportunity to discuss this with your instructor and classmates in the first laboratory class.

1. I will work cooperatively with my classmates, both by listening and giving thought to others' ideas, as well as contributing my own ideas. I will do my share of the work as I expect others to do their share.

2. I understand that using one's own words when writing promotes understanding and learning. I will regularly record my ideas and questions in my own words during lab.

3. I understand that giving concise and accurate oral presentations is a useful skill to have. I will take advantage of the opportunities in this class to develop that skill.

4. I expect to share data with my team members. With the exception of shared data, I will write assignments by myself, using my own words. I will prepare my own graphs, figures, or charts and do my own interpretations, and will not represent others' work as my own, even during group projects or presentations.

5. I will abide by The University of Georgia's Academic Honesty standards as outlined in *A Culture of Honesty*. It is my responsibility to familiarize myself with the current UGA academic honesty policies as they apply to BIOL 1103L.

NOTICE OF PARTICIPATION IN A MANDATORY COURSE FIELD TRIP

6. I hereby acknowledge my awareness that my participation in the BIOL 1103L field trip to test water quality may expose me to risk of property damage and bodily or personal injury that may prove fatal. Examples of risks that I may be exposed to include: traffic accidents, falls, drowning, insect bites, stings, snake bites, poison ivy, water-borne pathogens, etc., as well as other risks that may not be foreseeable. I hereby assume any and all such risks.

I hereby certify that I am at least 18 years of age and that I have read and understand and agree to abide by the guidelines described in this Biology 1103 laboratory manual.

_____

Signed   *Date*

WRITING IN BIOL 1103L

We sat down together to write a few paragraphs about why you will be required to write in a biology lab course. We had planned to write up a standard handout on the benefits of writing and so, naturally, we began to think about those benefits and what we wanted to say about them. This should have been a pretty easy task for us, since we are all fairly familiar with the benefits of writing in a science class. Yet, we had a hard time coming up with some specific reasons why you, as a student, should care about writing in Biology 1103L. And so, as we started to draw up an outline to list the points that we wanted to make, we realized that we were perfectly illustrating why writing is so important. Even though on some level we understand why writing in biology is essential to learning, forcing ourselves to write about why writing is important made us think more deeply about it. *That* is why we are asking you to write in a science class; not to torture you or to enforce ancient grammatical rules, but to force you to think hard about what you are writing about. We are going to ask you to do what we just did to ourselves. We are going to ask you to write, but mostly we are going to ask you to think. By going through this process of thinking and then writing we are confident that you will gain a better understanding of your experiments and the biology that underlies them than a bunch of problem sets could ever give you.

But everything we have told you so far applies to writing in general. All forms of writing force you to think about your subject. Why is writing particularly important in *this* class? One of the goals of this class is to teach you how to think like biologists, and the best way to understand how biologists think is to understand how they write. When a biologist writes a paper to inform her colleagues about an experiment she has done, the first thing she thinks about is the question she is trying to answer. Next, she thinks about the tests she did to try to answer that question and the results from those tests. Finally, she thinks about the conclusions that she can draw from her results, and she answers her question based on the evidence she has accumulated. That is how biologists think, and as a result, it is how they write. So, by writing about your experiments in this class you will have to think like a biologist; you will have to think about your question, your tests, and your observations, and you will have to think about the evidence that you use to answer your question.

Those are the real reasons we are asking you to write in this biology lab course.

Sincerely,

The BIOL 1103 lab staff

INTRODUCTION

The purpose of this laboratory class is twofold. One objective is to give you a chance to observe and explore, firsthand, some of the topics that you will be learning about in the lecture portion of the course. The second objective is to help you understand how scientific research is carried out by designing and performing your own experiments in the same way as practicing scientists. We know many of you have no desire to ever become scientists. However, carrying out a "scientific" investigation gives you a valuable insight into how scientific research is designed as well as knowledge that helps inform you about scientific advances and controversies that you will face as a patient, parent, and voting citizen.

Scientific Inquiry

Most of us are familiar with the stereotypical view of scientists: smart geeks who work alone in laboratories filled with test tubes and complicated equipment, conducting experiments that will instantly change life as we know it. Progress is usually made during dramatic "Eureka!" moments when the scientist has thought up a sudden and brilliant solution to a problem. Successful scientists have more "Eureka!" moments than unsuccessful ones.

The truth is far less dramatic. For starters, you do not need to be a genius to do science; almost anyone can do it. The primary difference between scientists and everyone else is that they have received a different type of training to do their work. Just as doctors and nurses are trained how to care for people's health, mechanics are trained how to fix and maintain engines, and farmers are trained how to plant, grow, and harvest different kinds of crops, scientists are trained to perform a specific type of job: observe and explain the world around us.

Scientists gather as much information as they can on a topic to try to explain what it is, how it works, why it does what it does, and in some cases, how much it is worth. Usually this information is collected in small pieces, and like parts of a complicated puzzle they must be put together in order to see the bigger picture. As more and more pieces are collected, our understanding of the topic being studied improves, and this knowledge can be used to create new products, solve problems, support a political agenda, or simply help us understand our surroundings a little bit better.

A second misconception about being able to "do" science is that doing science requires expensive and complicated equipment. In reality, the basic process of science is simply to determine if what we know and understand about an object or phenomenon is correct. To do this, you don't necessarily need any equipment at all. For example, if you think you might have left the stove on at home, you can do several experiments to determine if this assumption is correct simply by using your own senses. You can **look** at the controls to see if they are in the "on" position, you can hold your hand near the oven to **feel** if it is hot, you can **listen** to see if the gas burner inside the stove is active, or you can **smell** if there is gas. Additional tools, such as microscopes, balances, chemical tests, etc., largely serve to extend the limited range of our own bodies and senses.

One last misconception about scientists is that they are loners toiling away by themselves in isolated laboratories. Though some scientists can be socially challenged, most actually work as part of a team. Even in the few instances in which scientists do work alone, these scientists regularly discuss their work and share their ideas with others in order to receive constructive feedback. This process, called *peer evaluation*, is a critical part of science. Describing their work to others helps scientists catch or avoid mistakes in their own work. In addition, though they may be loath to admit it, someone else might have a better idea or has gathered new information that causes them to rethink their own.

In this class, we want you to be able to understand how scientists carry out investigations as well as to carry out a few investigations of your own. We hope that after the semester is over you will be able to more effectively evaluate some of the "scientific" claims you are bombarded with every day (What's the most effective way to lose weight? Is global warming real or not? Does Enzyte® really work?). In addition, we want you to learn how to find out answers for yourselves on scientific topics that are important to you.

Scientific Reasoning

The basic goal of science is to explain our surroundings as accurately and completely as possible using the tools available. Many people think the primary way of doing this is by conducting experiments. In reality, experiments are only a small part of the process that scientists follow when they try to learn more about an object or process. Two additional, and arguably more important, parts are **Observation** and **Reasoning**.

Observation is relatively straightforward. It includes gathering all of the information you have available on the topic that you are examining. This can include information that you have collected yourself (seen, heard, smelled, measured, etc.) as well as information that is provided by others (other scientists, your instructor, etc.).

Reasoning is a little more complicated. First, it involves thinking. Second, there are two distinct types of reasoning: inductive and deductive.

Inductive reasoning involves taking the specific information you have gathered so far through observation (details) and trying to draw some general conclusions (the big picture). This is often done by organizing the information into manageable categories or by looking at how the different pieces of information fit together. An inductive leap occurs when you are able to take the specific information you have collected and can formulate a general principle. For example, if you look at a magazine and see specific articles discussing various kinds of exercise and healthy dinner recipes, you might come to the general conclusion that this is a magazine for readers interested in healthy living.

Deductive reasoning is the reverse of inductive reasoning. General assumptions are used to draw specific conclusions. In other words, if a general principle you are following is correct, you should be able to make specific predictions about the topic you are studying. This process can be described as using "if...then" statements. For example, *if* we assume the magazine we are looking at is aimed at readers interested in healthy living, *then* we might expect to find specific articles commonly found in a magazine about healthy living.

It is only after a scientist has made a prediction through deductive reasoning that they actually do an experiment. The purpose of the experiment is to see if the prediction that has been made is supported. In the case of our magazine, a simple experiment might be to look at the table of contents to see what articles are listed. If there are articles on topics such as healthy snacks, new exercises, ways to relieve stress, etc., which are commonly found in magazines about healthy living, the predictions would have been met and general assumption would be supported. If the predicted articles are not found, it would be necessary to rethink the general assumption that had been made (perhaps it's not a magazine about healthy living).

It is important to point out that meeting predictions does not **prove** that a general assumption is correct. It just means that additional information that you have obtained continue to **support** the general assumption. It is possible that closer examination may reveal more information that might disagree with your general assumption. For example, you might notice that most of the fitness articles are about tennis; this would indicate that the magazine is actually aimed at tennis players in particular.

The general process of solving scientific problems using both inductive and deductive reasoning is often referred to as the *Scientific Method*. It has the following steps:

1. Observe a phenomenon and gather information.
2. Develop general assumptions about the phenomenon from available information.
3. Make a specific prediction(s) that should be true if the general assumption is correct. In these "if…then" statements, the "if" part is generally referred to as a *hypothesis*.
4. Develop and conduct an experiment to test your hypothesis.
5. Reassess the general assumption based on the hypothesis and results of the experiment.
6. Repeat steps 1–5 as needed until you are confident that your general assumption is correct.
7. Share your findings with others.

Even though the *Scientific Method* is stated in a rigid format it does not normally function in that fashion. Every scientist develops a personal approach that can be fairly different than the one stated above. Therefore, in this and our other biology laboratory courses, we use the phrase "*The Scientific Process*." Regardless of the approach, however, the outcome is the same—the support or non-support of the hypothesis based on experimental results.

LABORATORY 1

SCIENTIFIC INVESTIGATIONS: NATURE OF SCIENCE

THE CHECKS LAB: STUDENT INSTRUCTIONS AND ASSESSMENT

Read the following instructions for the next activity. Do not move on until instructed to do so. Questions should be answered as a group with one final set turned in to your GLA.

Names of group members:

Date:

GLA:

INTRODUCTION

This activity is designed to help you experience the **nature of science (NOS)**. The NOS describes the characteristics of what science is and how scientific knowledge is built. For example, one characteristic of science is that it is built on evidence that can be observed or inferred from the natural world. Another characteristic of science is that the people gathering that evidence (scientists) never work alone. These may seem to be simple principles, but sometimes the evidence that scientists gather is confusing, seemingly conflicting, and apparently random. Furthermore, each new bit of evidence often creates more questions than it answers.

---

1 Steve Randak and the ENSI website http://www.indiana.edu/~ensiweb/lessons/chec.lab.html

This activity will illustrate that scientific explanations are only tentative because new discoveries may show that previous hypotheses were not supported. It also will demonstrate the value of collaboration within working groups and with other groups in order to arrive at a reasonable explanation of a problem.

There is at least one other characteristic of science that is not usually appreciated or realized by people in the nonscientific community. See if you recognize it. Your lab instructor will ask about this at the end of lab today.

Directions and Assessment (6.5 points)

1. Each group will receive an envelope containing 16 checks written by fictional characters. Do not look at any of the checks until instructed to do so. When directed, and without looking at the checks in the envelope, remove **four** of the checks and place them on your lab bench. Do not allow other groups to examine your data at this time.

2. As a team, observe the information on the checks. Think of the checks as clues to a series of connected events. List the different types of information available in the space below. These can be listed in broad categories such as "information in memo lines of checks" or "business address on checks." **(0.5 points)**

3. With your group, formulate a tentative explanation for, or a storyline represented by, the four checks. The storyline should attempt to explain the events in the lives of the character(s) that wrote the checks. This is your **tentative explanation #1**. Record this below *with your evidence or rationale* for the explanation. **(1 point)**

4. When directed, remove and examine **four** more checks from the envelope. Is there any new information present that you did not have on the previous four checks? If so, record it below. **(0.5 points)**

5. Is your tentative explanation #1 supported by the information on these new checks? If so, use the space below to explain how it supports your tentative explanation #1. If not, does the new information require that you modify your first explanation, or does it require you to start over? Write your modified or new explanation (**tentative explanation #2**) below and include the supporting evidence. **(1 point)**

6. When directed, remove **two final checks** from the envelope. Record any new type of information, if present. **(0.5 points)**

7. Indicate below what changes need to be made in your working tentative explanation and the evidence supporting it. Then, write the new version of your explanation. **(1 point)**

8. Do not remove any more checks or look at the checks remaining in the envelope. Scientists never have all the data they might need to reach the highest level of confidence in their explanations.

9. To simulate the expanded collaborative nature of science, each group will be given a few minutes to meet with other groups to share data (information from checks). **All checks should be turned upside down or put away during this time; trading of checks between groups is not allowed.** Remember since each group drew at random, all groups may have some different data (this simulates the sharing of data and ideas by scientists through personal communication, email, etc.). *You are sharing your ideas and the information you have gathered from the checks, not the checks directly. Do not allow other groups to view your checks.*

10. What new information did you discover from other groups? **(0.5 points)**

11. When instructed, each group will come back together to formulate a final explanation based upon all the available data. This should explain the events in the lives of the characters that wrote the checks. Record this below. **(0.5 points)**

12. Choose a spokesperson to present your group's final explanation to the class: **this needs to be a *complete* story of the events in the lives of the characters that wrote the checks, not just a list of information**. This simulates the process of sharing scientific ideas in which all scientists engage at symposia and by publishing. **Be prepared to defend your explanation by using your data (the checks) and your rationale for reaching the explanation.** If you disagree with another group's explanation, you should ask them to defend their explanation, but you must be prepared to offer evidence that contradicts it.

13. After hearing the explanations from other groups, do you need to modify your explanation? If so, indicate how it is changed below and why you were convinced to change it. **(1 point)**

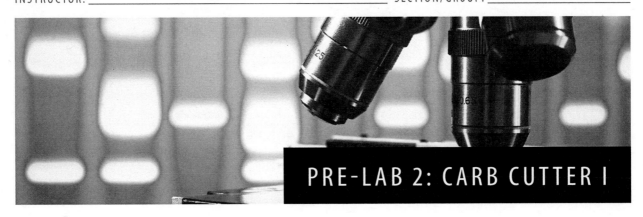

PRE-LAB 2: CARB CUTTER I

Note: All pre-lab assignments are due the day noted in the syllabus and are NOT subject to the 10%/day for late work policy as stated in the syllabus. You will not receive any credit for parts of this assignment that are incomplete or not attempted.

Important Information

The following equation relates concentration and volume and is critical for calculating dilutions:

Concentration $_{initial\ stock\ solution}$ × Volume $_{initial\ stock\ solution}$ = Concentration$_{final\ solution}$ × Volume $_{final\ solution}$

OR

$$C_I \times V_I = C_F \times V_F$$

How to use this equation: If you have an initial concentration of sugar at 500 mg/ml and you want to make 100 ml of a solution with a sugar concentration of 250 mg/ml, you would use the equation as follows:

$$C_I \times V_I = C_F \times V_F$$

500 mg/ml × ***What Volume?*** = 250 mg/ml × 100 ml

Instructions: In order to successfully complete the three-week Carb Cutter lab module, you will need to practice quantitative and data collection skills. Part 1 of this week's Pre-lab Homework focuses on the quantitative skills: concentrations, standard curves, and dilutions. Part 2 focuses on qualitative and quantitative data collection.

Helpful Charts

Weight Measured in Grams (g)	Volume Measured in Liters (L)
(mg) milligram = 1/1000 g	(ml) milliliter = 1/1000 L
(µg) microgram = 1/1000 mg	(µl) microliter = 1/1000 ml
(ng) nanogram = 1/1000 µg	(nl) nanoliter = 1/1000 µl

Conversion Example

$$\frac{500\ mg}{liter} = \frac{500\ mg}{liter} \times \frac{1\ liter}{1,000\ ml} = \frac{500\ mg}{1000\ ml} = \frac{0.5\ mg}{ml}$$

PART 1: CONCENTRATIONS, STANDARD CURVES, AND DILUTIONS

Concentrations

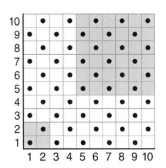 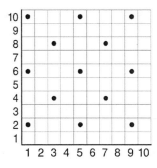

1. The graphs above show the distribution of dots in two 10 × 10 cm² grids (cm not drawn to scale, but you should use cm² for your unit of measurement in this problem.)

   a. Which grid has a higher concentration of dots? **(0.5 points)**

   b. Give the concentration of dots in both grids. Report in units of dots/cm2. **(0.5 points)**

   Grid A:

   Grid B:

   c. In Grid A, which area has the higher concentration of dots: the 2 × 2 cm² section in the lower left corner or the 6 × 6 cm2 section in the upper right corner? How do their concentrations compare to the concentration of the whole grid? **(0.5 points)**

   d. Based on your observations in Question 1c, what can you conclude about changes in dot concentration when grid area varies? **(0.5 points)**

2. Give the concentrations in units of mg/ml for the following solutions. Full credit will not be awarded if your calculations are not shown below. **(2 points)**

	50 g/liter	0.5 g/ml	5 mg/ml	500 mg/liter
Concentration in mg/ml				

Show your work here:

Standard Curve

3. You are building a go-cart for the National Go-cart Championship Race. Knowing that heavier go-carts travel faster but consume more gas, you need to figure out the optimal go-cart weight. This graph shows the relationship between the weights of last year's go-carts and the amount of gas they used. Use the graph to answer questions a–d.

Gas Consumption Depending on Car Weight

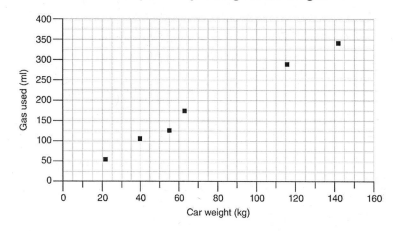

a. What overall conclusion can you draw from the data depicted in this graph? **(0.5 points)**

b. How much gas would a 40 kg go-cart use? **(0.5 points)**

c. Predict how much gas a 100 kg go-cart would use. Show how you determined this. **(0.5 points)**

d. You buy a tank that holds 200 ml of gas. What is the maximum weight your go-cart can have to consume exactly 200 ml of gas? **(0.5 points)**

Dilutions

Concentrations and volumes are NOT the same thing. Concentrations are in units of mass/volume (i.e., g/L or mg/ml). Volumes are in units of *only* volume (i.e., L, ml).

4. a. If you mixed 265 g of sugar with water to get a final volume of 725 ml, what is the concentration of this solution in g/L? Show your work. **(1 point)**

$$\frac{g}{ml} \times \frac{ml}{L} = \frac{g}{L}$$

b. If you took 1 ml of this solution, what would the concentration be? Explain your reasoning. **(1 point)**

5. You prepare a **stock solution** (highly concentrated) of sugar in water whose concentration is 500 g/L. You need to make a new solution that is half (1/2) as concentrated and has a final volume of 100 ml. Describe how you would make this dilution (show all work in the space provided). **(2 points)**

Hint: Use the $C_I \times V_I = C_F \times V_F$ formula to help you solve the problem.

Step one: Your new solution has a concentration of _____.

Step two: To make 100 ml of this new solution, you will need to add _____ (ml) of concentrated stock solution plus _____(ml) of water.

Hint: Calculate your volume based on your stock solution. Water is a "filler" that you add to reach final volume.

Now make a second solution that is one-tenth (1/10) as concentrated as the initial stock solution and has a final volume of 100 ml. Describe how you would make this dilution (show all work in the space provided). **(2 points)**

Step one: Your new solution has a concentration of _____.

Step two: To make 100 ml of this new solution, you will need to add _____ (ml) of concentrated stock solution plus _____ of water.

PART 2: QUANTITATIVE AND QUALITATIVE DATA COLLECTION

How Do You Relate Glucose, Weight Loss, and Carb Cutter?

As an intrepid reporter for the *Red and Black*, you have been given the assignment of writing an exposé on a new fad on campus—the use of a weight-loss supplement called Carb Cutter. **Carb Cutter is touted for its ability to block the normal digestion of starch.**

Starch, a large carbohydrate, is normally broken down by the **enzyme amylase** into glucose molecules. Glucose is preferentially used by the body for energy instead of fat, thus hampering the process of weight loss. Carb Cutter contains an ingredient extracted from northern kidney beans (*Phaselous vulgaris*) that prevents the proper functioning of amylase. If amylase cannot work, starch cannot be digested into glucose, and therefore gets eliminated by your body.

How do enzymes work? Enzymes are proteins that **catalyze** (speed up) chemical reactions in our bodies. Their amino acids fold to create small pockets with unique shapes called "active sites." Only molecules with the correct corresponding shape can fit into these active sites and take part in the reaction promoted by the enzymes. To speed up all of the different chemical reactions you need to live, your body produces over 5,000 different enzymes.

METHODS FOR DETECTING STARCH

Qualitative data allow you to **estimate relative values**. Quantitative data allow you to **measure specific values**.

QUALITATIVE METHODS: COLOR CHANGE

Iodine-potassium iodide (I_2KI) solution contains a mixture of iodine (I_2) and potassium iodide (KI) and has a yellowish-orange color. If I_2 inserts into the middle of the helical structure of intact amylose (starch and glycogen) molecules, the solution changes to a bluish-red color. Amylose is a part of starch and is a polysaccharide. This color change does not occur with smaller carbohydrate fragments because they do not have the necessary helical structure.

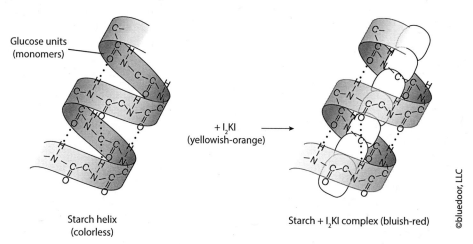

Glucose units (monomers)

+ I_2KI (yellowish-orange)

©bluedoor, LLC

Starch helix (colorless)

Starch + I_2KI complex (bluish-red)

Quantitative Methods: Spectrophotometry

A **spectrophotometer** is a machine that measures the amount of light absorbed by or transmitted through a solution. It accomplishes this by shining a beam of light from one side of the tube to a light detector on the other side. The detector measures how much light actually passed through the tube. If a lot of light is absorbed by the solution, then little light was transmitted through it to the detector. Inversely, if little light is absorbed, a lot of light was transmitted through. Here's a graph of the relationship:

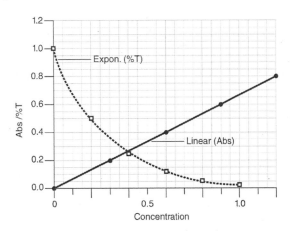

Absorbance readings are in numerical values of 0 to 2. Surprisingly, these values do not have units but instead are interpreted according to known standard curves.

Why is the spectrophotometer set to a particular wavelength (580 nm)?

An important part of using a spectrophotometer accurately is to set it at the appropriate wavelength (measured in nanometers, or nm). Every substance absorbs different wavelengths of light; all other light wavelengths either pass through the substance or bounce off the substance. Clear solutions absorb very little light, thus making it difficult to obtain absorbance measurements. In the Carb Cutter lab module, you will be working with clear starch solutions. However, as you just learned, when I_2KI binds to starch it brings about a color change. Thus, adding this dye to your starch solutions will make it easier to obtain absorbance values. The solutions in this lab absorb at a wavelength of **580 nm**. You will calibrate your spectrophotometer to read only your solution of interest by creating a "blank" tube. **Your blank will contain volumes of all solutions in your experiment *except* your variable of interest.**

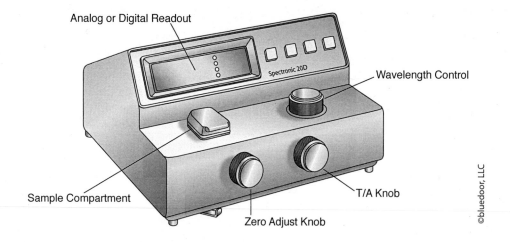

Analog or Digital Readout

Spectronic 20D

Wavelength Control

Sample Compartment

Zero Adjust Knob

T/A Knob

©bluedoor, LLC

Your GLA will demonstrate how to use a spectrophotometer.

6. a. When using a spectrophotometer and measuring a solution in a sample tube, the spectrophotometer indicates 100% transmittance. What does this mean? **(0.5 points)**

    b. What is a blank tube, and what is it used for? **(0.5 points)**

    c. You want to measure the concentration of starch in your samples and need to create a blank tube. Would you include I_2KI? Why or why not? **(0.5 points)**

7. When measuring starch samples *in a spectrophotometer*, what would you expect to see if (Hint: Remember relationship between absorbance and concentration.)

    a. one tube contained more starch than the other? **(0.5 points)**

    b. there was the same concentration of starch in both tubes? **(0.5 points)**

    c. there was no starch in one tube? **(0.5 points)**

8. *Without using a spectrophotometer,* how would you determine if one solution was more concentrated than the other? **(0.5 points)**

9. How could you use the spectrophotometer to determine the starch concentration in the two test tubes in terms of g/L? **(2 points)**

Hints:

- Remember you can make a graph using a standard curve.
- You will have a stock solution of starch available to make dilutions if required, as in Question 5.

LABORATORY 2

CARB CUTTER I EXPERIMENT

Group Members:

Objective 1: Use a *qualitative* method to determine whether starch is present in four solutions [A–D] and, if so, the relative concentration of starch in each solution.

Background

On your lab bench, there are four solutions, labeled in bottles A, B, C, and D, containing unknown concentrations. It is possible that one of the solutions does not contain starch. Discuss and agree on an approach with your group that will allow you to:

1. determine whether or not there is starch in the solutions, and

2. place test tubes A–D in order of lowest to highest starch concentrations.

   Read the "Available Tools and Equipment" AND "Ideas to Consider" sections below. Then in your group, determine a plan to carry out your experiment. Fill out the Experimental Design Section on page 16 and show it to your GLA BEFORE you begin.

Available Tools and Equipment

- Four bottles, labeled A–D, each containing a starch solution of unknown concentration
- I_2KI (you will need 0.3 ml to stop the reaction)
- Syringes of different volumes (note that syringes are labeled with colored tape)
- Spectrophotometer tubes and corks
- Test tube rack
- Tris buffer
- Stock starch solution (concentration: 10 g/L)

IDEAS TO CONSIDER

- Before you begin your experiment, practice using the syringes to draw up liquid and release it. Be careful and exact in your measurements. Notice that the syringes have different numbering systems (1 cc = 1 ml).

- Why is it important to use a different syringe for each solution?

- How much liquid does a test tube hold?

- **You will need at least 4 ml of solution in your tubes for accuracy.**

Objective 1 Experimental Design and Qualitative Results

Carry out your experiment and take notes below describing what you did and how your experiment helped you achieve Objective 1. Your descriptions should be clear and complete enough so that someone else can follow your logic and repeat your tests if necessary. **Although you should discuss this as a group, your written work should be your own and will be graded as such by your GLA.**

EXPERIMENTAL DESIGN (3 POINTS)

- **Objective:** What are your experiments designed to find?

- **Prediction:** What sort of results do you expect to see if the tubes have varying starch concentrations?

- **Procedure:** Provide sufficient detail so that another classmate could replicate your methods.

Results

- **Evidence:** Describe the data and observations used to answer your questions.

- **Explanation:** Explain how your evidence helped (or did not help) you to answer your questions.

- **Thinking Forward:** What potential sources of error were there in this experiment? What follow-up experiment would you do?

CARB CUTTER I EXPERIMENT

Objective 2: Use a *quantitative* method to determine whether starch is present in four solutions [A–D] and, if so, the absolute concentration of starch in these solutions.

Background

The results you obtained from the previous experiment are *qualitative*. They tell you which solutions have more/less starch than others but not much more than that. Often, it's desirable to obtain more precise data—*quantitative* results. How would a spectrophotometer help you do this?

Please read the "Available Tools and Equipment" AND "Ideas to Consider" sections below. Using notes from your pre-lab assignment as a guide, discuss and agree upon an approach with your group to carry out your experiment. Fill out the Experimental Design Section on page 19 and show it to your GLA BEFORE you begin.

AVAILABLE TOOLS AND EQUIPMENT

- Four bottles, labeled A–D, each containing a starch solution of unknown concentration
- I_2KI (you will need 0.3 ml to stop the reaction)
- Tris buffer
- Stock starch solution (concentration: 10 g/L)
- Syringes
- Spectrophotometer tubes and corks
- Test tube rack
- Spectrophotometer

IDEAS TO CONSIDER

- What information will the spectrophotometer tell you about your solutions?
- How does this information translate to absolute concentration values?
- Can you think of a way to relate absorbance values to corresponding starch concentrations using a standard curve that has been created with known values?
- **You will need at least 4 ml of solution in your tubes for accuracy.**

Objective 2 Experimental Design and Quantitative Results

Carry out your experiment and take notes below describing what you did and how your experiments helped you achieve Objective 2. Your descriptions should be clear and complete enough so that someone else can follow your logic and repeat your tests if necessary. **Although you should discuss this as a group, your written work should be your own and will be graded as such by your GLA.**

Graph paper is available to use on the next two pages.

When you are done, please dump and wash test tube contents down the sink. Wash out your tubes and place back in test tube racks.

Experimental Design (3 points)

- **Objective:** What are your experiments designed to find?

- **Prediction:** What sort of results do you expect to see if the tubes have varying starch concentration?

- **Procedure:** Provide sufficient detail so that another classmate could replicate your methods.

Results

- **Evidence:** Describe the data and observations used to answer your questions.

- **Explanation:** Explain how your evidence helped (or did not help) you to answer your questions.

- **Thinking Forward:** What potential sources of error were there in this experiment? What follow-up experiment would you do?

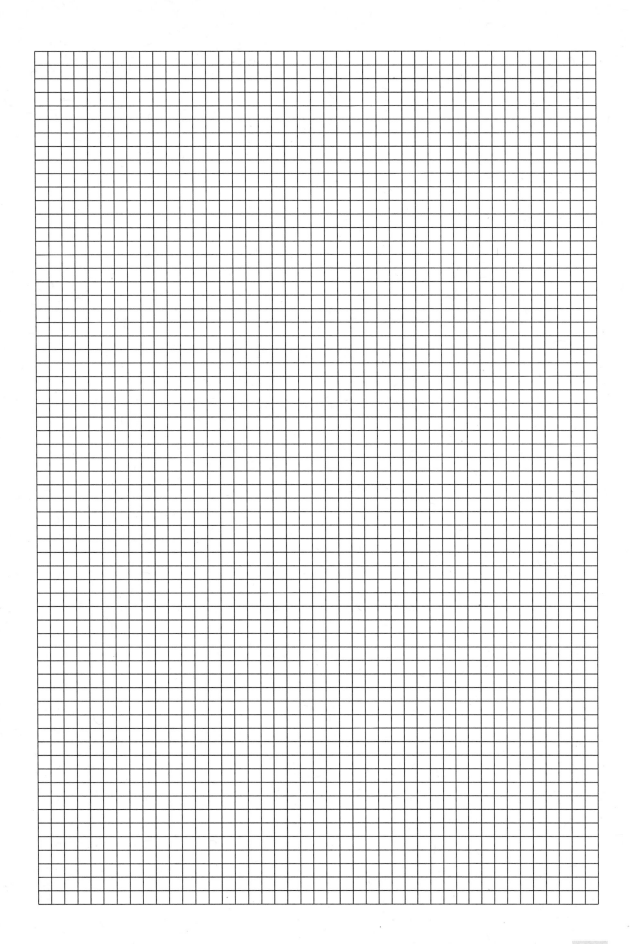

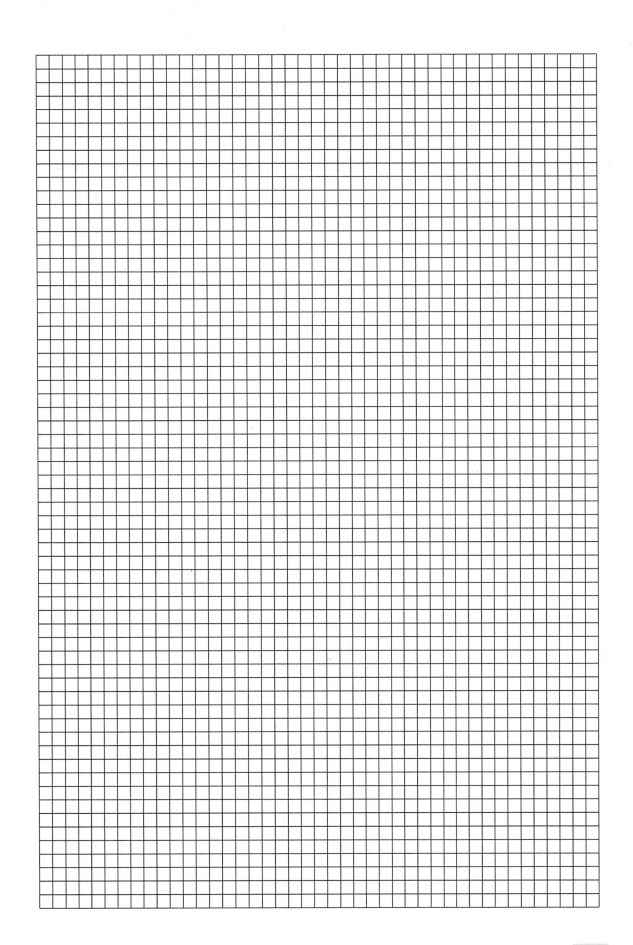

PRE-LAB 3: CARB CUTTER II

Note: All pre-lab assignments are due the day noted in the syllabus and are NOT subject to the 10%/day for late work policy as stated in the syllabus. You will not receive any credit for parts of this assignment that are incomplete or not attempted.

Instructions: In the previous lab, you were asked to determine the absolute concentration of starch in a set of test tubes. To do this successfully you needed to create and use graphs of your data. Below are some problems that will give you practice creating and using graphs.

1. You work in the lab at a local hospital. It's Saturday evening, and a large part of your night will be spent determining blood alcohol levels for patients in the emergency room. To do this, you use a spectrophotometer and a chemical that changes color when it reacts with alcohol. Using a set of alcohol solutions as known values you obtain the following results (Note: for this exercise we are using % blood alcohol as our "concentration" of alcohol in an individual's blood):

% Blood Alcohol	Absorbance (ABS)
0.01%	0.03
0.02%	0.05
0.05%	0.15
0.1%	0.22
0.2 %	0.55
0.5 %	1.25

a. Use this information to prepare a standard curve below, including proper axis labels, title, and units. **(1.5 points)**

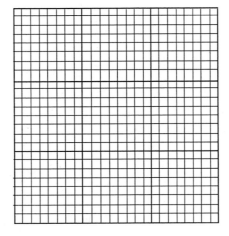

b. Use your standard curve in Question 1a to determine blood alcohol levels for these five patients. **(2.5 points)**

Patient	Symptoms	Absorbance	% Blood Alcohol
1	Poor balance, impaired memory and speech	0.20	
2	Lightheaded, talkative	0.05	
3	Comatose, respiratory distress	1.1	
4	Nauseous, uncoordinated	0.45	
5	Semiconscious	0.7	

2. The graph below shows a standard curve for starch. Use it to answer the following questions:

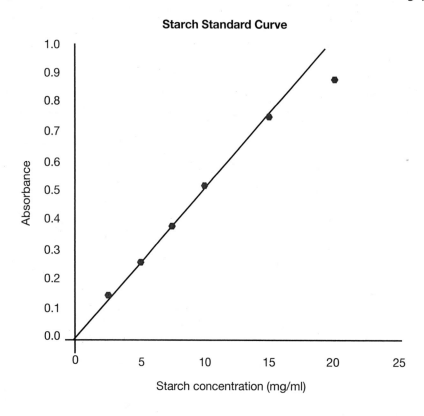

Starch Standard Curve

a. You have two tubes (I and II) that initially contain the same concentration of starch. However, you add one microgram (1 µg) of amylase enzyme to Tube II and then let both tubes sit for ten minutes. The resulting absorbance value for Tube I is 0.74 and for Tube II is 0.56. Why do you see a difference between the two samples? **(0.5 points)**

b. What is the starch concentration in each tube? Combining your new knowledge from both tubes, what is the **rate** at which the starch was digested (report in mg/ml per time)? **(1 point)**

c. How much starch do you think would be in Tube II if you let it sit for thirty minutes instead of ten? Explain your answer. **(0.5 points)**

d. The manufacturers of the Carb Cutter pill claim that it blocks the ability of amylase to digest starch. If you had included Carb Cutter in Tube II at the beginning of your tests, how much starch would you predict would be present after 30 minutes? **(0.5 points)**

LABORATORY 3

CARB CUTTER II EXPERIMENT

Group Members:

Objective 1: Is Carb Cutter effective at preventing amylase enzyme from digesting starch?

Background

Using your Pre-lab Homework exercise, discuss and agree upon an approach with your group that will allow you to determine if Carb Cutter prevents amylase from digesting starch.

Please read the "Available Tools and Equipment" AND "Ideas to Consider" sections below. Then in your group, determine a plan to carry out your experiment. Fill out the Experimental Design Section and show it to your GLA BEFORE you begin.

Available Tools and Equipment

- I_2KI (you will need 0.3 ml to stop the reaction)
- Tris buffer
- Stock starch solution (concentration: 10 g/L)
- Amylase solution (concentration: 3 g/L)
- Carb Cutter solution (5 ml total needed)
- Syringes
- Spectrophotometer tubes and corks
- Test tube rack
- Spectrophotometer
- Reaction mixture bottle

IDEAS TO CONSIDER

You will need to know the answers to these in order to accomplish Objective 1.

- How do you determine if the given amylase is working as expected?

- **What are appropriate amounts of each solution to use?**

  Remember, you will need the following equation to help you determine the volumes of starch and amylase you need:

  $$\text{Concentration}_{\text{initial stock solution}} \times \text{Volume}_{\text{initial stock solution}} = \text{Concentration}_{\text{final solution}} \times \text{Volume}_{\text{final solution}}$$

The final volume of your reaction solution needs to be 30 ml.

- How much starch will you need if the final concentration of starch for this experiment is 7 g/L?

- How much amylase will you need if the final concentration of amylase for this experiment is 0.1 g/L?

- How much Tris buffer is needed to bring the final volume of the reaction solution to 30 ml?

Once starch and amylase have been combined, the reaction has begun! Adding I$_2$KI will immediately stop amylase activity.

- This lab is about Carb Cutter, but you have not actually used it yet! If Carb Cutter claims to stop enzyme activity, how will you test this?

- The instructions on the Carb Cutter bottle advise you to take the pill 15–20 minutes before eating a meal. *Why* do you need to take this into account when planning your experiment? *How* will you do this?

- What trend do you expect to see the longer you let the reactions run?

- After you determine absorbance values, you're still missing critical information: concentration of starch present. How can you relate absorbance values to concentration values? *Hint:* Think about Objective 2 from last week's lab.

Use 4–5 ml of reaction mixture solution in each tube for accuracy…just be sure to use the same amount in EVERY tube.

- What solution(s) belong(s) in your "blank tube" for the experiment you described above?

Objective 1 Experimental Design and Results

Carry out your experiment and take notes below describing what you did and how your experiments helped you achieve Objective 1. Your descriptions should be clear and complete enough so that someone else can follow your logic and repeat your tests if necessary. **Although you should discuss this as a group, your written work should be your own and will be graded as such by your GLA.**

When you are done, please dump and wash test tube contents down the sink. Wash out your tubes and place back in test tube racks.

EXPERIMENTAL DESIGN (2.5 POINTS)

- **Objective:** What are your experiments designed to find?

- **Prediction:** What sort of results do you expect to see as time progresses?

- **Procedure:** Provide sufficient detail so that another classmate could replicate your methods.

Results

- **Evidence:** Describe the data and observations used to answer your questions.

- **Explanation:** Explain how your evidence helped (or did not help) you to answer your questions.

- **Thinking Forward:** What potential sources of error were there in this experiment? What follow-up experiment would you do?

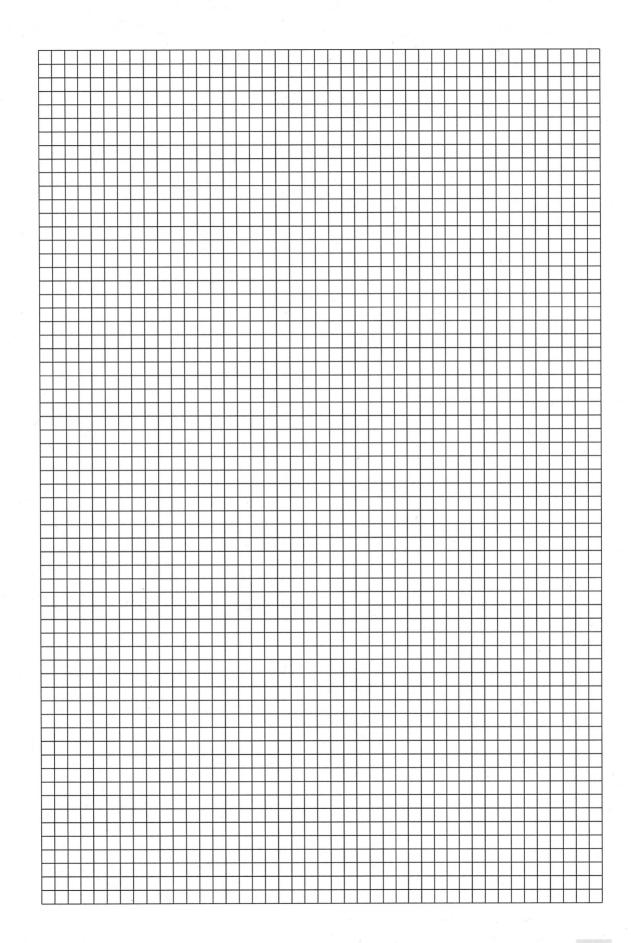

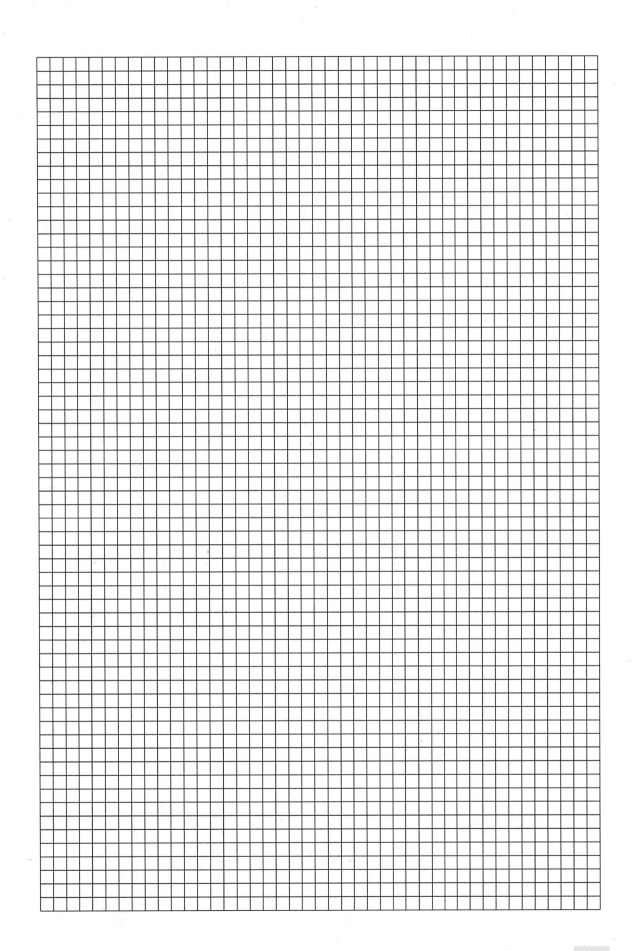

LABORATORY 4

ANTIBIOTIC RESISTANCE I:
OF BIRDS AND BACTERIA

Note: All pre-lab assignments are due the day noted in the syllabus and are NOT subject to the 10%/day for late work policy as stated in the syllabus. You will not receive any credit for parts of this assignment that are incomplete or not attempted.

Pre-lab Reading

Instructions: Read the two articles that follow (*Of Birds and Bacteria* and *It's Just a Flesh Wound*) and answer the questions that follow each article.

Bacteria are found in all corners of the globe and can survive in almost any imaginable environment. They are also a critical component of any healthy ecosystem.

- Bacteria break down organic material and release nutrients for other organisms.
- Bacteria found in our gut help with digestion processes.
- Beneficial bacteria help protect our bodies from pathogens.
- Bacteria are responsible for most of the photosynthesis on earth (blue-green algae).
- Bacteria fix atmospheric nitrogen gas in the soil to form compounds that plants use as fertilizer.
- Bacteria are used for bioremediation (cleaning up toxic waste) in the environment.
- Commercially, bacteria are used in a wide assortment of products such as cheese, yogurt, bioplastics, pharmaceuticals, detergents, and a variety of chemicals.
- Bacteria even help sculpt the surface of the earth by producing acids that speed up erosion of rocks into dirt.

Unfortunately, not all bacteria are so helpful. Some pathogenic species can cause disease ranging from mild skin irritation to life-threatening illness. For example, strains of *Staphylococcus* can commonly be found on the skin and in the nose, upper throat, large intestine, and vagina. *Staph* is normally harmless but some pathogenic strains can cause impetigo, abscesses, sties, and boils. They have also been implicated in cases of food poisoning, Toxic Shock Syndrome, pneumonia, and life-threatening blood infections.

In the following Pre-lab Assignment, you will learn about two other pathogenic strains of bacteria: *Campylobacter* and *Salmonella*.

OF BIRDS AND BACTERIA

"Superbugs" that resist the usual antibiotic treatments are nasty, and they could be in your chicken dinner. Here's how to protect yourself.

From *Consumer Reports*, January 2003

In the fall of 1997, almost three-fourths of the broilers that Consumer Reports bought in stores nationwide harbored salmonella or campylobacter—the bacteria most likely to give Americans food poisoning. Our new tests revealed contamination in about half of the chickens we analyzed, but there's a dark cloud within that silver lining. Many of the contaminated chickens harbored strains of salmonella and campylobacter that are resistant to antibiotics commonly used against those bugs, which can cause fever, diarrhea, and abdominal cramps.

As a result, the estimated 1.1 million or more Americans sickened each year by undercooked, tainted chicken, or by food that raw chicken juices have touched, may stay sick longer, possibly with more serious illnesses. Doctors may have to prescribe several antibiotics before finding one that works. And patients may have to pay more to be treated.

Antibiotics—which may include, experts say, low doses of human drugs such as penicillin, erythromycin, and tetracycline—are given to chickens to prevent or reduce sickness and to speed growth. That practice is based on studies dating to the 1950s that showed animals given antibiotics reach their market weight faster, though perhaps only a day faster, than untreated animals.

When birds actually get sick, perhaps with respiratory disease from *Escherichia coli* picked up from their own droppings, they need full-strength antibiotics for a short time. Flocks are too big for veterinarians to treat individual birds, so all birds may receive antibiotics in their drinking water.

These drugs kill not only the bacteria that cause chickens to become sick, but also some of the many other types of bacteria that normally live inside chickens. Their routine use in so many birds sets the stage for the evolution of drug-resistant microbes that multiply around chicken coops, each of which can hold up to 20,000 birds. Bacteria that survive drug treatment may eventually contaminate carcasses during slaughtering and processing. And if chicken isn't cooked thoroughly enough to kill those bacteria, they could end up on your dinner plate, then colonize your intestines.

You need swallow just 15 to 20 salmonella bacteria, or about 500 campylobacter, to become ill. Both bugs can cause intestinal distress. Campylobacter can also cause serious complications, including meningitis, arthritis, and Guillain-Barré syndrome, a severe neurological disorder.

Copyright © 2003 by Consumers Union of U.S., Inc. Yonkers, NY 10703-1057, a nonprofit organization. Reprinted with permission from the January 2003 issue of Consumer Reports® for educational purposes only. No commercial use or reproduction permitted. www.ConsumerReports.org.

Once the bacteria are in you, they may stay, living peacefully in your digestive tract only to cause hard-to-treat disease when transferred to the bloodstream or urinary tract. Danish researchers recently found that when healthy volunteers ate just one meal contaminated with antibiotic-resistant strains of the bacterium *Enterococcus faecium* that came from chicken or pork, the bug lingered in the volunteers' intestinal tracts for up to 14 days. Antibiotic-resistant *E. faecium* does not cause disease if confined to your intestines, but if it escapes into your bloodstream, say during surgery, it can be fatal.

Although stronger-than-usual or extended doses of antibiotics might eventually kill the bugs in most people, resistant germs can be risky for the very young, the very old, and people with weakened immune systems.

For what is, to our knowledge, the largest nationally representative analysis of antibiotic resistance in store-bought chicken, we tested 484 fresh, whole broilers bought at supermarkets and health-food stores in 25 cities nation- wide last spring. Represented in our tests were 4 leading brands (*Foster Farms, Perdue, Pilgrim's Pride, and Tyson*), 14 supermarket brands, 9 premium brands (usually from smaller companies, usually more expensive, labeled as raised without antibiotics, and including free-range and organic brands), and 2 kosher brands.

Our shoppers packed the raw birds in coolers and shipped them overnight to a lab. There, tests determined whether salmonella and campylobacter were present, showed whether those bacteria were resistant to a range of human antibiotics, and measured the chickens' total plate count, an indicator of spoilage.

HOW CONTAMINATED?

The percent of tested chickens that harbored the two main foodborne disease-causing bacteria is shown below. For each major brand, we analyzed, on average, about 75 chickens; for supermarket brands, we analyzed a total of 75; for premium brands, a total of 82. If salmonella and campylobacter hitched a ride on the same carcass, consumers would have a good indication of what not to buy, but the presence of the two bugs often didn't track, as is evident with Pilgrim's Pride. Brands are ranked based on contamination with campylobacter, which is more prevalent than salmonella and more likely to be resistant to common antibiotics.

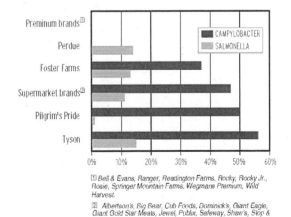

[1] Bell & Evans, Ranger, Readington Farms, Rocky, Rocky Jr., Rosie, Springer Mountain Farms, Wegmans Premium, Wild Harvest.

[2] Albertson's, Big Bear, Cub Foods, Dominick's, Giant Eagle, Giant Gold Star Meats, Jewel, Publix, Safeway, Shaw's, Stop & Shop White Gem, Tops, Trader Joe's, Wegmans.

KEY FINDINGS:

No major brand was less contaminated than others overall. *Pilgrim's Pride* had an exceptionally low incidence of salmonella but, along with *Tyson*, a higher incidence of campylobacter than most other brands.

All 12 samples from Ranger, a premium brand sold only in the Northwest, were free of campylobacter and salmonella. Ranger's chickens also had among the fewest bacteria that can cause spoilage.

HOW RESISTANT?

To qualify for our test of antibiotic resistance, a chicken had to be contaminated with campylobacter or salmonella. We then tested whether those germs were resistant to major antibiotics often used to treat people. "Somewhat resistant" means that the growth of bacteria on a sample of chicken was inhibited, but not stopped, by an antibiotic at a normal dosage.

If you were to become infected with such bacteria, it could take longer—or require more than the typical dosage—for antibiotics to cure you. "Resistant" means that the bacteria survived a normal dose of the antibiotic and would therefore continue to make you sick. Your doctor would then have to prescribe a different antibiotic and hope that it would do the trick.

Tests of antibiotic resistance were performed on campylobacter from 155 chicken samples and on salmonella from 58 chicken samples. Because the relatively small sample size limits the meaningfulness of differences among brands and even categories of chicken, the table shows drug sensitivity across all samples. Antibiotics are in alphabetical order.

Antibiotic	Campylobacter		Salmonella	
	Somewhat Resistant	Resistant	Somewhat Resistant	Resistant
Ampicillin	–	–	0%	19%
Ceftriaxone	–	–	10	0
Ciprofloxacin	1%	26%	0	0
Clindamycin	8	21	–	–
Erythromycin	45	20	–	–
Gentamicin	2	8	0	5
Nalidixic acid	–	–	0	3
Ofloxacin	0	26	–	–
Tetracycline	1	66	0	17
Trimethoprim sulfamethoxazole	–	–	0	0

Antibiotic resistance: The Animal Health Institute, which represents manufacturers of animal drugs, says antibiotic resistance is a top concern. But it maintains that the use of antibiotics in food animals poses an extremely small risk to human health and that the increase of bacterial resistance to antibiotics in humans is largely the result of over-reliance on antibiotics in human medicine.

A spokesman for the National Chicken Council, an industry group, notes that "a very large percentage" of antibiotics used in chickens are not closely related to any drugs used in humans. The council also points to data indicating that the overall usage of antibiotics in animals of all kinds has been declining since 1999.

Indeed, four of the biggest U.S. poultry producers recently announced that they have reduced their use of certain antibiotics. Last year, *Tyson* said it had "chosen to discontinue its previously minimal use" of fluoroquinolone antibiotics in broiler chickens. *Perdue* says it stopped using fluoroquinolones last year. *Foster Farms* says it stopped using them approximately five years ago and does not give other important human drugs to chickens except when they're sick. *Pilgrim's Pride* says it stopped using fluoroquinolones in October 2000.

Margaret Mellon, director of the food and environment program at the Union of Concerned Scientists, a nonprofit environmental group, applauds any cut in antibiotic use. "You don't ever want to use antibiotics where you don't need them," she says. "The rule in antibiotics is, if you use them you lose them." But Mellon points out that industry data don't provide specifics about antibiotic use and production that would be helpful in monitoring ways to prevent drug resistance. The government doesn't collect such data, either. "We know nothing," she says. "We are flying blind."

Moreover, although the use of fluoroquinolones may have tapered off, at least nine other antibiotics are approved for use in both chickens and humans, and some are used in substantial quantities. For example, the Union of Concerned Scientists estimates that more than 380,000 pounds of erythromycin are given to poultry every year to hasten growth and prevent disease.

Despite the chicken producers' announcements and the premium-chicken label claims, our tests support the need for continued concern. Our tests showed that if you are sickened by one of those chickens, two commonly used antibiotics—tetracycline, an older but still important drug used against germs from pneumonia to chlamydia, and erythromycin, an option for patients allergic to penicillin—may not help. In 66 percent of the campylobacter- contaminated chickens, the bacteria were resistant to tetracycline. In 20 percent, they were resistant to erythromycin.

Your chances of being cured by the usual doses of two fluoroquinolones, ciprofloxacin and ofloxacin, may also be limited. The latest figures from the FDA, reported in 2001, indicate that 11,477 Americans were infected in 1999 by fluoroquinolone-resistant campylobacter in chicken.

Antibiotic-resistant campylobacter appeared even in chickens from the two brands labeled "certified organic," Rosie and Springer Mountain Farms. That isn't as surprising as it might sound. Although antibiotics are not allowed in organic poultry, and farmers must demonstrate to organic certifiers that they have not been used, antibiotic-resistant bacteria are ubiquitous and can persist in the environment for years. In any case, we learned after our tests were finished that Springer Mountain Farms had taken the organic claim off its label.

In 19 percent of the chickens contaminated with salmonella, the bacteria were resistant to ampicillin, used against a dozen or more different bacterial infections. In 17 percent, bacteria were resistant to tetracycline.

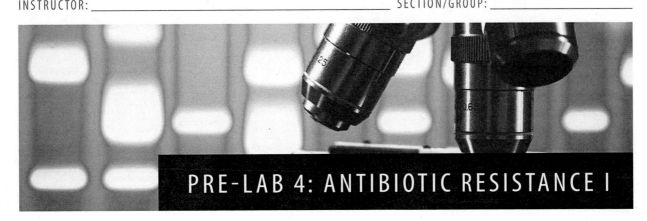

PRE-LAB 4: ANTIBIOTIC RESISTANCE I

Questions 1–2

1. **Context:**

   a. What were the two main objectives of this study? **(1 point)**

   b. Aside from taking antibiotics yourself, how else might you come in contact with bacteria that have been exposed to antibiotics? **(0.5 points)**

   c. How would organisms in the wild be exposed to antibiotics? **(0.5 points)**

2. **Results:** What were the major findings of the experiments? **(2 points)**

"It's Just a Flesh Wound."

All bacterial cells have a plasma membrane surrounded by a cell wall. Some bacterial strains have an additional plasma membrane outside of this cell wall. Bacteria that **do not** have this second plasma membrane can be stained with crystal violet in a technique developed by Hans Gram for the identification of Gram- positive or Gram-negative bacteria. Stained bacteria are called **Gram-positive**, and unstained bacteria are called **Gram-negative**. An example of Gram-positive bacteria is *Staphylococcus (Staph)* and an example of Gram-negative bacteria is *Escherichia coli (E. coli).*

Doctors are seeing an increasing number of patients who are infected with bacteria that are resistant to many of the antibiotics prescribed today. This **antibiotic resistance** in bacteria makes it much more difficult to successfully treat infections. Some bacteria exposed to antibiotics can change and the antibiotic no longer affects it. This bacteria will thrive and replicate, producing more bacteria that are resistant to that specific antibiotic.

Below is an example of how *Staph* bacteria develop resistance to a commonly prescribed antibiotic, Penicillin.

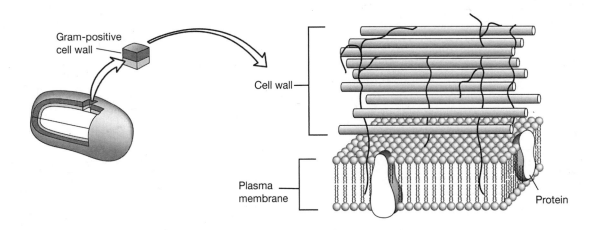

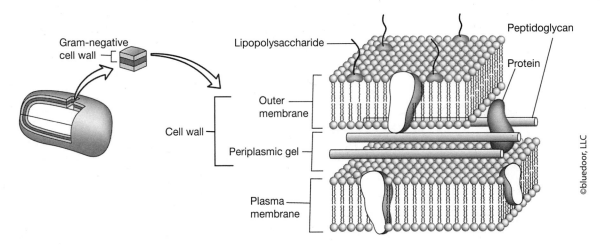

©bluedoor, LLC

Figure 4.1. Cell wall and gram staining.

Peptidoglycan is a carbohydrate-protein mixture found in cell walls of bacteria. An enzyme called transpeptidase is required for building peptidoglycan. In *Staph*, the antibiotic penicillin inhibits transpeptidase, thereby preventing the formation of their cell walls. Most bacteria cannot survive without a cell wall so exposure to penicillin should kill all *Staph*. However, some *Staph* make slightly different versions of transpeptidase that are only slowed down by penicillin, not stopped; these versions are more resistant to penicillin. If a person stops taking penicillin too soon, the bacteria with the more resistant versions of transpeptidase will survive and multiply because penicillin will kill the less resistant versions. If this person were to take penicillin again, this antibiotic would be less effective in fighting off a *Staph* infection because most of the bacteria would now make the more resistant form of the transpeptidase enzyme: **the population has evolved antibiotic resistance.**

Note: Some bacteria *can* survive without a cell wall, but this means they have no peptidoglycan.

Question 3

3. You are a doctor working at a local hospital. A few of your patients have been admitted for recurring infections and need treatment. The hospital pathologist has isolated and characterized the bacteria involved in each of the infections. *Table 4.1* below gives a list of commonly used antibiotics, the characteristics of bacteria that they work against, and how they work against the bacteria (mechanism of action). **Broad-spectrum antibiotics** work against both Gram-positive and Gram-negative bacteria. **Narrow-spectrum antibiotics** are only effective against specific families of bacteria. The pathologist's report of your patients is *Table 4.2*. Using both of these tables, which antibiotic would you prescribe for each patient and why? ***There is more than one correct answer for each patient, but you only need to report one.*** (3 points)

Table 4.1. Common antibiotics and their properties.

Antibiotic	Spectrum	Mechanism of Action (How the antibiotics work against bacteria)
Penicillin (P)	Broad (Gram +,* some Gram –)	Inhibits enzyme for cell wall formation
Oxacillin (OX)	Narrow (Gram +)*	Inhibits enzyme for cell wall formation **Same family and mechanism of action as penicillin**
Amoxicillin-clavulanic acid (Augmentin®)	Broad (Gram +,* some Gram –)	Amoxicillin inhibits peptidoglycan formation; clavulanic acid inhibits beta- lactamases that destroy amoxicillin
Cefazolin	Broad (Gram +, * some Gram –)	Inhibits peptidoglycan formation by binding to the enzyme transpeptidase
Vancomycin	Narrow (Gram +)*	Inhibits the synthesis of peptidoglycan
Gentamicin	Narrow (Gram –; a few Strep. are susceptible)	Inhibits protein synthesis
Tetracyclines	Broad (Gram +/–) (Gram +; rickettsia and chlamydia)	Inhibits protein synthesis
Rifampin	Broad (Gram + ; mycobacteria)	Blocks RNA synthesis by binding and inhibiting RNA polymerase
Trimethoprim-sulfa-methoxazole (Bactrim™)	Broad (Gram +,–)	Inhibits folic acid synthesis (required for survival of bacteria)
Polymyxin B	Narrow (Gram –)	Binds to cell membrane and disrupts its structure and permeability
Streptomyocin	Broad (Gram +,–)	Inhibits protein synthesis in both Gram +,–

* Gram + (antibiotic works against
Gram-positive bacteria) Gram – (antibiotic works against Gram-negative bacteria)

Table 4.2. Pathologist's report.

Patient	Bacteria Characteristics	Antibiotic Prescribed
#1	Gram (+), no cell wall, Tetracycline resistant.	
	Rationale:	
#2	Gram (–), cell wall present, Amoxicillin and Gentamicin resistant.	
	Rationale:	
#3	Gram (+), cell wall present, Penicillin resistant, patient is allergic to tetracycline.	
	Rationale:	

Questions 4–6

You may need to use outside resources to help you answer the next three questions:

4. How can overuse of prescribed medications lead to antibiotic resistance? **(0.5 points)**

5. How can not finishing a prescribed round of antibiotics lead to antibiotic resistance? **(0.5 points)**

6. This week you will test *Bacillus subtilis* (*B. subtilis*) (Gram +) and *E. coli* (Gram –) to see if either is resistant to commonly used antibiotics and antibacterial products. What is the difference between an antibiotic and an antibacterial? **(1 point)**

BACTERIA: TURN YOUR HEAD AND COUGH

A major problem that we face today is that different strains of bacteria are rapidly becoming more and more resistant to commonly prescribed antibiotics. You will be completing two Antibiotic Resistance activities where you will test two strains of bacteria against common antibiotics and antibacterial products. These two strains of bacteria are *E. coli* and *B. subtilis*. Before you conduct these tests, however, you will need some practice in collecting and growing bacteria.

How do you culture bacteria? Selective media that promote the growth of some bacteria and prevent the growth of others have been developed to isolate specific bacterial strains. To grow **bacteria** during the first part of this experiment, you will use **mannitol (sugar) + salt agar** (red Petri dishes), a medium that has a high salt concentration and promotes the growth of harmless bacterial strains rather than harmful ones.

Bacteria are everywhere, but you want to collect bacteria from one specific source. To ensure that you do not contaminate your Petri dish with bacteria from multiple sources, you need to use **sterile (aseptic) technique** when preparing your cultures.

POINTERS FOR WORKING UNDER STERILE CONDITIONS

- Work with bacteria and Petri dishes in the **designated area** of the lab room. It's easier to maintain sterility if the area you're working in is small.

- **Keep all equipment sterile** (the bacterial cultures, Petri dishes, and other instruments). **Put on disposable gloves.** While your hands are gloved, try not to handle anything that is not sterile (i.e., your lab manual, your pencil, or any part of your body).

- **Open the Petri dish as little as possible.** If you must put the Petri dish lid down, place it on the bench with the outside portion of the lid facing up.

- **Avoid coughing, sneezing, or breathing directly into the Petri dish, bacterial cultures, or other sterile equipment.**

- **Use a sterile swab to collect the bacteria** from *one place* of your choice (skin, mouth, lab bench, bathroom, bottom of your shoe, etc.).

Your GLA will demonstrate how to spread your sample onto an agar plate using aseptic technique before you begin your collections.

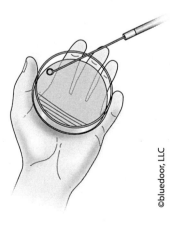

©bluedoor, LLC

ANTIBIOTIC RESISTANCE I EXPERIMENT

Objective 1: Which antibiotics/antibacterials are most effective at preventing *B. subtilis* (Gram +) and *E. coli* (Gram −) growth?

Background

Using an approach for culturing bacteria that is similar to the mannitol (sugar) + salt agar plates that you just used, two different types of bacteria have been cultured for the experiment you are about to develop and carry out: *E. coli* (a Gram − bacteria) and *subtilis* (a Gram + bacteria). Discuss your answers to Pre-lab 6 with your group. Agree upon which antibiotics and antibacterial products you will use in your experiment.

> **Please read the "Available Tools and Equipment" AND "Ideas to Consider" sections below. Then in your group, determine a plan to carry out your experiment. Fill out the Experimental Design Section and show it to your GLA BEFORE you begin.**

Available Tools and Equipment

- Mueller-Hinton agar bacterial growth plates (one plate per student)
- Liquid cultures of *B. subtilis* and *E. coli*
- Filter discs presoaked in antibiotics
- Blank filter discs
- Antibacterial products
- Sterile water
- Sterile tweezers
- Sterile cotton swabs
- Markers
- Gloves

Ideas to Consider

You will need to know the answers to these in order to accomplish Objective 1.

- Each student in a group has their own plate. How does this benefit your experiment?

- Will you put both *B. subtilis* and *E. coli* on one plate, or just one of the bacterial strains? Why?

- What would be a good control for this experiment?

- Would you consider different controls for antibiotics versus antibacterials?

Method: How to Perform an Antibiotic Disc Diffusion Assay

STEP ONE: CREATE A BACTERIAL LAWN ON A PETRI DISH

In order to test your bacterial cultures, you need to spread them out onto Mueller- Hinton agar bacterial growth plates. This is called making a **bacterial lawn**, the technique for which is described below. Practice aseptic method when creating your lawns.

1. Put on gloves.

2. Obtain your plate and label the bottom with the bacteria you are going to spread.

3. Obtain your tube of bacteria. Do not hold it by the lid!

4. Gently roll the tube between the palms of your hands to resuspend the bacteria.

5. Obtain a package of sterile cotton-tipped swabs. Remove **one** from its packaging.

6. Remove the tube lid and stick the end of the swab into the bacteria until it is sufficiently soaked. Remove the tip and close the lid.

7. Remove the lid from your plate and gently wipe the swab over the entire surface of the plate. You should lift the lid as little as necessary. This should deposit bacteria picked up from the culture onto the agar. Be sure to wipe the *entire* surface of the plate.

8. As the bacteria grow over the next day or two they will form a distinct layer on the surface of the agar; this is your bacterial lawn.

STEP TWO: INTRODUCING DISCS WITH ANTIBIOTICS/ANTIBACTERIALS

Once you have created your lawn and it has dried, it is time to test the antibiotics and antibacterial products.

1. Sterilize your tweezers with an alcohol swab. Remove the lid from your plate and use a pair of sterile tweezers to transfer the antibiotic/antibacterial discs onto the agar plate.

2. Distribute four discs on the plate so that there is equal space in-between them. See figure below, for example.

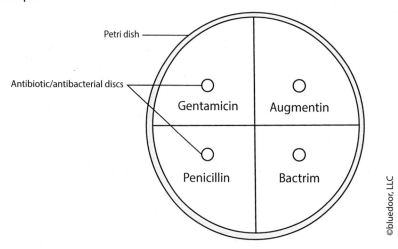

Figure 4.2. Petri dish with antibiotics/antibacterials.

3. Make sure the discs are lying flat on the plate by **gently tapping** them down with the sterile tweezers. DO NOT FORCEFULLY SHOVE THE DISCS INTO THE AGAR. DO NOT MOVE THE DISCS ONCE THEY ARE PLACED ON THE AGAR.

4. Put the finished plates in the collection area on the bench. A Lab Manager will place them in an incubator after lab is over.

OBJECTIVE 1: EXPERIMENTAL DESIGN

Carry out your experiment and take notes below describing what you did and how your experiments helped you achieve Objective 1. Your descriptions should be clear and complete enough so that someone else can follow your logic and repeat your tests if necessary. **Although you should discuss this as a group, your written work should be your own and will be graded as such by your GLA.**

Experimental Design (1.5 points)

- **Objective:** What are your experiments designed to find?

- **Prediction:** What results do you expect to see if the antibiotics/antibacterial products are working and why?

- **Procedure:** Provide sufficient detail so that another classmate could replicate your methods.

Bacteria: _____   Bacteria: _____

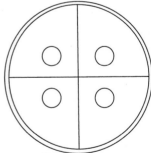   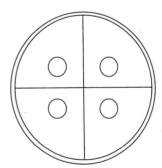

ANTIBIOTIC RESISTANCE II: AND THE ANSWER IS...

Note: All pre-lab assignments are due the day noted in the syllabus and are NOT subject to the 10%/day for late work policy as stated in the syllabus. You will not receive any credit for parts of this assignment that are incomplete or not attempted.

Instructions: Read the two sections that follow (*Basis of the Antibiotic Disk Assay and Determining Sources of Fecal Pollution*….) and answer the questions on the pages that follow the reading selections.

Questions 1–3

BASIS OF THE ANTIBIOTIC DISK ASSAY

In the previous lab, you transferred disks saturated with antibiotics/antibacterial products to agar plates that had been spread with bacteria. Exposure to moisture in the agar causes the substances in the disks to diffuse into the agar resulting in a gradient of antibiotic concentration. Bacteria resistant to the concentration of antibiotic they encounter will survive, while those susceptible to the concentration of antibiotic they encounter will die. The area in which bacteria are susceptible will appear as a clear area around the disk and is referred to as the **zone of inhibition**. This assay has been standardized such that, by measuring the diameter of the zone of inhibition, you can determine whether the plated bacteria are resistant or susceptible to a particular antibiotic or something in between. Information for specific antibiotics is provided on the following page.

1. The diagram below shows a plate of four antibiotic disks placed on an *E. coli* bacterial lawn. The disks are represented by black dots and the zones of inhibition are the clear areas around the disks. Using a ruler, measure the diameter of the zones of inhibition for each disk **in mm**. Based on this data, which antibiotic is most effective against E. coli? Explain how you drew your conclusion. **(2 points)**

Zone of inhibition measurements

Penicillin _____

Augmentin _____

Gentamicin _____

Bactrim _____

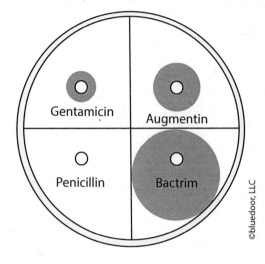

©bluedoor, LLC

For the next two questions, refer back to Lab 6, as necessary, to review the following information:

Staph is a surface bacteria. It is found on body surfaces such as skin, eyes, and mouths that interact with an external environment. Alternatively, *E. coli* is primarily found in the digestive tract. Finally, bacteria are categorized as Gram + or Gram −, and this is due to the presence or absence of the secondary cell membrane. These categorizations only apply to bacteria.

2. You are given two Mueller-Hinton agar plates. One has a bacterial lawn of *E. coli* (Gram −) and the other has a bacterial lawn of *Staph* (Gram +). Each is treated with a disk soaked in Listerine. After incubating the plates two days at 37 °C, the zone of inhibition in the *Staph* plate is 40 mm whereas the zone of inhibition in the *E. coli* plate is 5 mm. Why is Listerine more effective on *Staph*? Why is the zone of inhibition bigger for *Staph* than for *E. coli*? **(1 point)**

3. The *Staph* that you collected from different sources was grown on agar plates with a high salt concentration (red plates). This salt concentration specifically selects for *Staph* and prevents other bacteria from growing on these plates. Why do you think that *Staph* is more resistant to high salt concentration? **Hint: Remember where *Staph* is found. For example, what happens when you sweat? (1 point)**

Questions 4–9

APPLIED AND ENVIRONMENTAL MICROBIOLOGY, Dec 1999,p.5522–5531   Vol. 65, No12

DETERMINING SOURCES OF FECAL POLLUTION IN RURAL VIRGINIA WATERSHED WITH ANTIBIOTIC RESISTANCE PATTERNS IN FECAL STREPTOCOCCI

CHARLES HAGEDORN, *SANDRA L. ROBINSON, JENNIFER R. FILTZ, SARAH M. GRUBBS, THERESA A. ANGIER, AND RAYMOND B. RENEAU, JR.

Department of Crop and Soil Environmental Sciences, Virginia Polytechnic Institute and State University, Blacksburg, Virginia 24061

Received 4 June 1999/Accepted 12 September 1999

Nonpoint sources of pollution that contribute fecal bacteria to surface waters have proven difficult to identify. Knowledge of pollution sources could aid in restoration of the water quality, reduce the amounts of nutrients leaving watersheds, and reduce the dangers of infectious diseases resulting from exposure to contaminated waters. Patterns of antibiotic resistance in fecal streptococci were analyzed by diskriminate and cluster analysis and used to identify sources of fecal pollution in a rural Virginia watershed. A database consisting of patterns from 7,058 fecal streptococcus isolates was first established from known human, livestock, and wildlife sources in Montgomery County, Va. Correct fecal streptococcus source identification averaged 87% for the entire database and ranged from 84% for deer isolates to 93% for human isolates. To field test the method and database, a watershed improvement project (Page Brook) in Clarke County Va., was initiated in 1996. Comparison of 892 known-source isolates from that watershed against the database resulted in an average correct classification rate of 88%. Combining all animal isolates increased correct classification rates to ≥95% for separations between animal and human sources. Stream samples from three collection sites were highly contaminated, and fecal streptococci from these sites were classified as being predominantly from cattle (>78% of isolates), with small proportions from waterfowl, deer, and unidentified sources (~7% each). Based on these results, cattle access to the stream was restricted by installation of fencing and in-pasture watering stations. Fecal coliforms were reduced at the three sites by an average of 94%, from prefencing average populations of 15,900 per 100 ml to postfencing average populations of 960 per 100 ml. After fencing, <45% of fecal streptococcus isolates were classified as being from cattle. These results demonstrate that antibiotic resistance profiles in fecal streptococci can be used to reliably determine sources of fecal pollution, and water quality improvements can occur when efforts to address the identified sources are made.

Table 5.1. Patterns of antibiotic resistance of fecal streptococci from known sources

Drug and concn (µg/ml)	% Resistant Isolates from Each Source					
	Beef cows (n = 1,398)	Chickens (n = 824)	Dairy cows (n = 728)	Deer (n = 1,245)	Humans (n = 1,579)	Waterfowl (n = 1,284)
Chlortetracycline (40)	1	90	17	0	78	1
Erythromycin (15)	0	77	0	0	76	0
Neomycin (10)	2	100	100	0	54	0
Oxytetracycline (10)	90	100	100	38	98	97
Streptomycin (60)	96	100	100	59	100	97
Tetracycline (15)	81	100	80	0	87	2

n, total number of isolates from each source

Answer the following questions using the preceding article, "Determining Sources of Fecal Pollution in a Rural Virginia Watershed with Antibiotic Resistance Patterns in Fecal Streptococci" from *Applied Environmental Microbiology*, December1999.

4. What is **non-point source pollution**? **(0.5points)**

5. Give two reasons why it is important to stream and watershed health to determine non-point sources of pollution? **(0.5 points)**

6. Following the identification of cattle as the source of the contaminating bacteria, cattle were restricted from the area. Did fencing lower the bacterial contamination? **(0.5 points)**

7. You want to determine if the source of fecal contamination is from dairy cows or wild deer. Which antibiotic would give you the most clear results and why? **(1 point)**

8. Why are so few bacteria isolated from waterfowl (e.g., geese and ducks) resistant to antibiotics? **(0.5 points)**

9. You conduct a similar test on water collected from three different local sources and obtain the results detailed in *Table 5.2.*

Table 5.2.

Drug and concn (μg/ml)	% Resistant Isolates from Each Source		
	Tanyard Creek, Athens-Clarke County (*n* = 975)	Oconee River, Madison County (*n* = 1,013)	Bent Creek, Oconee County (*n* = 563)
Chlortetracycline (40)	77	100	0
Erythromycin (15)	76	70	0
Neomycin (10)	50	100	5
Oxytetracycline (10)	100	93	27
Streptomycin (60)	95	100	45
Tetracycline (15)	87	95	8

n, total number of isolates from each source

Use the data patterns of antibiotic resistance from known sources in *Table 5.1* to answer the following question: What would you conclude is the likely source of fecal bacteria for each location? **(1.5 points)**

Location	Source
a. Tanyard Creek	
b. Oconee River	
c. Bent Creek	

10. Why did you choose these sources? **(1 point)**

AND THE ANSWER IS...

Last week you collected bacteria from a specific source and spread them out onto a selective growth media: mannitol (sugar) + salt agar. The media contains food for bacteria (sugar) and a solid substrate (agar) on which they can grow. Most types of bacteria cannot handle the high salt concentration present in this media, and hence, will not grow very well. However, *Staphylococci* strains (commonly found in and on our bodies) thrive in this environment. Over time, each *Staphylococcus* bacterium on the plate grows and reproduces until a colony (ten to hundreds of thousands of bacteria) is formed. Do you have evidence of *Staph* colonies on your plate?

Write-up of Antibiotic Resistance Experiment

Examine the plates from the experiment you conducted last week on exposure of *B. subtilis* and *E. coli* isolates to antibiotics/antibacterial products. Answer the following questions for the bacteria you tested

1. **Evidence:** Create a table showing your data. **(1 point)**

2. **Explanation:** After evaluating this data and comparing it to the class data table generated, what is the answer to the question you posed during your experimental design? **(2 points)**

3. Antibiotic Resistance Infographic/Flyer **(6 points)**

   Now that you have completed the Antibiotic Resistance lab module, you will create a flyer or infographic about current medical diseases that display antibiotic resistance. The flyer/infographic will be created based on your knowledge of how antibiotic resistance evolves and the work you performed in lab using different antibiotics and antibacterial products.

   This is a group assignment; pairs of students will turn in one flyer/infographic. Each member of the pair will receive the same grade. A rubric and examples are available in eLC.

GLOSSARY OF TERMS

Agar: a polysaccharide, usually extracted from red algae that is used as a solidifying agent in the preparation of culture media.

Commensalism: a symbiotic relationship in which one organism is helped but the other organism is neither helped nor hurt.

Indicator: an organism whose presence indicates the condition of an environment.

Inoculate: the process of aseptically transferring bacteria from one medium to another.

Parasitism: a symbiotic relationship in which one organism (the parasite) benefits at the expense of the other organism (the host).

Plate: a technique in which a small volume of bacterial cells is transferred to the center of an agar plate and spread evenly about the plate using a glass spreader or similar tool.

Selective medium: culture medium that favors the growth of specific bacteria; this may be accomplished by inhibiting the growth of undesired bacteria or by encouraging the growth of only the desired bacteria.

Symbiosis: an ecological relationship between two different species of organism that live together in direct contact.

Zone of inhibition: the clear area around an antibiotic disk that results from susceptibility of bacteria to the antibiotic.

LABORATORY 6

EVERYBODY OUT OF THE POOL I: WATER QUALITY TESTING[1]

LAB SECTIONS THIS WEEK WILL BE AT A FIELD SITE.

Your GLA will provide you with information on where you will meet and how to get there.

Class will start promptly five minutes later and end five minutes earlier than normal to allow for travel time. Please make every effort to arrive on time. Lab classes will meet unless The University of Georgia is closed or weather conditions are deemed unsafe for outdoor activities (check the 1103L eLC page for information on the day of your lab if you are concerned).

If you arrive at the designated field trip site and your GLA is not present, please take the following measures:

1. Wait for 15 minutes. If your GLA has not arrived, call the people listed above to make them aware of your lab section's situation. They will attempt to locate your GLA. Leave messages if you cannot reach anyone.

2. Wait another 15 minutes. If your GLA or a substitute instructor has not arrived at the end of this 30-minute period, please call the people listed above to make them aware of your lab section's situation.

---

1 Water testing protocols and forms reproduced courtesy of Georgia Adopt-A-Stream Manual. http://georgiaadoptastream.org

Safety

Exploring a natural area entails safety concerns that differ from those of a laboratory setting. During this field trip there will be no smoking or swimming. Always be within sight of at least one other person who is aware of your presence. Do not leave the field trip sites before the end of class.

Dress Code

If you have questions or concerns about the dress code, be sure to ask your GLA BEFORE the day of your lab.

It is strongly suggested that you cover yourself from your torso down; this means a shirt that covers your middle, long pants, socks, and closed-toed shoes (old sneakers work well). Light colored clothing and long sleeved shirts are recommended to reduce insect bites and exposure to poison ivy. Please wear clothes and shoes that you don't mind getting dirty. Disposable ponchos will be provided at the lake in rainy weather. Dress appropriately, realizing that you will be outdoors significantly longer than it takes to walk to class. You will not be permitted to "run home" for something you forgot, so make sure you will not be uncomfortable.

WHERE DOES OUR DRINKING WATER COME FROM?

If you exited east out of Sanford Stadium and walked the distance of a couple football fields, you'd eventually have to cross the north fork of the Oconee River, which, along with the Bear Creek Reservoir and the Middle Oconee River, provides the source for our drinking water. But where does the water in the Oconee River come from?

In this week's lab we will explore a local natural watershed during a field trip. A watershed can be defined as "The area of land where all of the water that falls in it and drains off of it goes to a common outlet." (USGS, https://www.usgs.gov/, 2016). Not only is a healthy watershed important for the environment, but the locations we are visiting also feed into Athens' drinking water. We will be using the Georgia Adopt-a-Stream Manual protocols. Not only will we be giving to the community by monitoring the water quality, but you should also be able to take this knowledge and use it to monitor a stream or river in your own hometown.

You will be working in groups, so you will have to choose one of four aspects of the water quality monitoring to work on this week and be prepared to present on the data you collect next week.

Group	Section in the Lab Manual	Pages
Group 1	I. Land uses and activities	73-74
	II. General water body and watershed assessment	75-76
	III. Pipe and drainage ditch inventory	76-77
Group 2	IV. Physical sampling: Settleable solids; Turbidity; Air and water temperature; Dissolved oxygen	77-78
	Forms to fill out	83
Group 3	V. Chemical sampling: Coliscan Easygel kit; pH and Alkalinity; Nitrates; Orthophosphates	78-79
	Forms to fill out	83
Group 4	VI. Macroinvertebrate Sampling	79-80
	Forms to fill out	85

Web Resources for Your Presentation

All groups will find the "Getting to Know Your Watershed Manual" extremely helpful for their presentations. To access this informtion:

1. Go to https://adoptastream.georgia.gov/
2. Click on the Georgia Adopt-a-Stream icon. Choose **Materials and Resources**, and then **Manuals, Forms, etc.** Scroll down to find the Manual.

Additional helpful sites include:

- **The Upper Oconee Watershed Network (watershed maps - Group 1)**
- **Chattahoochee River National Recreation Area, Environmental Factors (Groups 2 and 3)**
- **USGS (U.S. Geological Survey) (Groups 2 and 3)**
- **Georgia Adopt-A-Stream Visual Steam Survey Manual (Group 4)**

Safety

Here are several safety tips that you should review before you begin your field trip.

- **Listen to and heed severe weather reports.** If thunderstorms are predicted, check eLC for updates from your GLA about how to proceed.
- **If you drive, park in a safe and legal location.**
- **Never wade into swift or high water.** Wear shoes that are in good condition and have bottoms that provide good traction. Do not walk on unstable stream banks.
- **Stay with your group members!** Always monitor with at least one partner, and let your GLA know immediately if someone is injured.
- **Watch out for poisonous plants.** Poison ivy, poison sumac, and poison oak love to grow along streams, so we advise that you wear long sleeve shirts and pants, and take special precautions when moving through underbrush. There are poison ivy wipes in each group's bucket to use if you come in contact with the plants.

©Shutterstock

- **Be wary of the water from the stream.** Wash with antibacterial soap before eating or drinking if your hands have been in contact with stream water. Treat every stream as if it were polluted; wear waders, rubber gloves, and goggles.

- **Leave the nature area better than you found it.** This field trip is mostly about examining, observing, and finally evaluating the quality of the watershed as a natural resource that needs be preserved for all Georgians. We will be trying to make as low an impact as possible on the area; remember that up to 600 students will be using this area each semester.

PRE-LAB 6: EVERYBODY OUT OF THE POOL I

You have signed up for one of the four groups for this week's lab. Before coming to lab this week read the article that follows and answer the questions that follow it.

WATER POLLUTION LINKED TO DOG DO

BYLINE: Traci Watson   USA TODAY   June 7, 2002

For as long as the dog has been man's best friend, dog waste has posed a menace to man's nose and foot. Now science has revealed a more unsavory truth: It's an environmental pollutant.

In the mid-1990s, scientists perfected methods for tracking the origin of nasty bacteria in streams and seawater. From Clearwater, Fla., to Arlington, Va., to Boise, the trail has led straight to the hunched-up dog—and to owners who don't pick up after their pets.

At some beaches, dogs help raise bacteria levels so high that visitors must stay out of the water. Goaded by such studies, some cities have directed as much as $10,000 in the past few years to encourage dog owners to clean up after their pets. A few municipalities have started issuing citations to those who ignore pet clean-up ordinances.

Many dog lovers are in denial about their pooches' leavings. But researchers have a name for the idea that areas used by dogs pump more bacteria into waterways: the "Fido hypothesis."

Dogs are only one of many fixtures of suburban America that add to water pollution. Lawn fertilizers, rinse water from driveways and motor oil commonly end up in streams and lakes.

But unlike those sources, dogs generate disease-causing bacteria that can make people sick. Studies done in the past few years put dogs third or fourth on the list of contributors to bacteria in contaminated waters. "Dogs are one of our usual suspects," says Valerie Harwood, a microbiologist at the University of South Florida. "At certain sites, we find their effect to be significant."

It doesn't take a Ph.D. to figure out that dog do is nasty. But it took science to determine how nasty it is. From mutt to blue-blooded champion, all dogs harbor so-called coliform bacteria, which live in the gut. The group includes *E. coli*, a bacterium that can cause disease, and fecal coliform bacteria, which spread through feces. Dogs also carry salmonella and giardia. Environmental officials use measurements of some of these bacteria as barometers of how much fecal matter has contaminated a body of water.

From USA TODAY, a division of Gannett Co., Inc. Reprinted with permission.

©Shutterstock

Lots of dogs and too few scoops. This wouldn't matter if pet dogs were as rare as pet chinchillas. But four in 10 U.S. households include at least one dog, according to the American Pet Products Manufacturers Association. The association's statistics also show that Americans owned 54.6 million dogs in 1996 and 68 million dogs in 2000. Of that total, 45% were "large" dogs—40 pounds or more.

Those numbers add up to a lot of kibble. That also wouldn't matter if all dog owners used a pooper-scooper. But several studies have found that roughly 40% of Americans don't pick up their dogs' feces (women are more likely to do so than men).

The environmental impact of dog waste went unrecognized for decades. Then scientists developed lab techniques to determine the origin of fecal bacteria contaminating water. One method is a variant of DNA fingerprinting. Another method looks at the antibiotic resistance of microbes from different species.

Scientists caution that the methods are still new. They are able to distinguish between major and minor sources of pollution, but they can't say with precision whether dogs contribute 20% or 30% of the pollution in a stream.

"There's inherently some error," says Don Stoeckel, a microbiologist for the Ohio district of the U.S. Geological Survey who is studying bacteria-tracking methods. "I think the best (they) can do is give you some evidence of the magnitude of each source."

Nonetheless, Stoeckel says, the analytical tools do provide useful information. Researchers have studied dozens of waterways. Wild birds and humans usually head the roster of who's fouling the water. But in some areas, dogs make significant deposits.

At Morro Bay, Calif., for example, dogs contribute roughly 10% of the *E. coli*, says Christopher Kitts, a microbiologist at California Polytechnic State University-San Luis Obispo. "And that can be the difference between a beach closing and a beach not closing," he says.

Places where dogs dirty the water:

- **Stevenson Creek in Clearwater, Fla.** Residents were worried that a sewage-treatment plant contaminated the creek. But when Harwood tested the water, she found that dogs, along with leaky septic tanks and wild animals, were to blame for high bacteria counts. Dog feces probably washed out of yards by the creek, Harwood says.

- **Four Mile Run in Arlington and Fairfax counties, Va.** Studies show that dogs add to the contamination in this suburban Washington, D.C., stream. Officials calculate that the 12,000 dogs living in Four Mile Run's watershed leave behind more than 5,000 lbs of "solid waste" every day.

- **Boise River in Boise.** The river suffers from high bacteria levels that make it unsuitable for swimming. Testing of streams and drainpipes flowing into the river showed that in urban areas, dogs were a leading culprit. In some spots, dogs and cats account for even more of the bacteria than human feces—from dysfunctional septic tanks and leaky sewage pipes—does.

Fines don't sway some. Even where dogs aren't the prime offenders, they're one of the few polluters authorities have control over. At many California beaches, for example, seagulls and other birds are most responsible for high bacteria levels. But federal laws protect birds.

That leaves dogs. Officials know that they have a lot of educating to do before people realize their pooch can be a canine sewage pipe. Some people find it humiliating to carry a plastic bag.

A survey by the Center for Watershed Protection in 1999 found that of the 41% of respondents who rarely or never clean up after their dogs, 44% would refuse to do so in the face of fines and neighbors' complaints. Reasons included "because it eventually goes away," "small dog, small waste," and "just because."

So more cities may follow the lead of Laguna Beach, Calif., a wealthy beach enclave. The city provides pooper-scoopers at the local dog park. But many people "don't take care of their little friends," says Victor Hillstead, the city's parks and buildings manager.

So the city hired Entre-Manure, a poop-scooping service based in nearby Dana Point whose motto is "#1 in the #2 Business." Since the city's contract started in January, the service has collected 187 pounds of dog waste from the city. "I'm real proud of that fact," says Craig Stern, founder and chief picker-upper. "That's pollution that'll never reach the ocean."

Cities want more to pick up 'piles.' Where they're cracking down:

San Diego. The city spent roughly $10,000 on extra trashcans, nagging signs and plastic "mutt mitts" at its Dog Beach, where the surf was closed to swimmers 125 times in 2000. The measures led to "measurably fewer 'dog piles.' That's the term we use," says Ted Medina, deputy director for coastal parks. He estimates the beach is 30%–40% cleaner than it was before the effort started late last year.

Chattahoochee River National Recreation Area near Atlanta. Bacteria levels in the river exceed standards so often that a Web site tells would-be boaters and swimmers whether the river is safe on any given day. To help clean it up, park officials recently started giving tickets to visitors who have dogs but no doggie bags.

Boulder, Colo. Here the problem wasn't dirty water but the nitrogen in dog droppings. Native grasses in the city's mountain parks are used to low-nitrogen conditions. But with dogs doing their business, weeds were muscling aside the grasses. The city did 10 months of education before starting to hand out $100 fines last year. Boulder officials had to convince residents that dog waste "is not fertilizer," says Mike Patton, co-director of open space and mountain parks. "Some people really did believe it was."

Provide answers in sentence-format to the following questions that are about the article you just read: "Water Pollution Linked to Dog Do." Each question is worth 0.5 points.

1. What is the "Fido hypothesis," and why is it a concern for waterways?

2. Besides dog feces, name three other potential sources of water contamination.

3. What step has been taken in the Atlanta area to limit dog droppings?

4. What is one method to limiting water pollution from dog feces that many individuals should use but do not?

5. How has the method that you put for the previous answer been shown to be successful?

6. What is one possible reason that the method you listed for the answer to question #4 has not been used?

7. Do increased fines for not picking up after your pet work? Why or why not?

8. For this week's lab, what is **your** lab group testing? For each test you list, *explain* why its measurements matter to the evaluation of water quality. (Note: You may need to look up your tests online.)

9. Brainstorm **three** questions that you would like to answer about Athens' watershed during lab.

WATERSHED SURVEY AND MAP ASSESSMENT

I. LAND USES/ACTIVITIES (GROUP 1)

When you first arrive at the site, fill out the following chart, checking all boxes that apply. Describe the location of the activity(ies) under Notes on Location and Frequency of Activities and also mark the location on the map.

Please indicate if you: ☐ surveyed only adjacent to the water body.
☐ surveyed the whole watershed.

Land Disturbing Activities and Other Sources of Sediment	Adjacent to Water	In Watershed	Notes on Location and Frequency of Activity
Extensive areas disturbed by land development or construction of utilities, roads, and bridges	☐	☐	_____
Large or extensive gullies	☐	☐	_____
Unpaved roads near or crossing streams	☐	☐	_____
Croplands	☐	☐	_____
Pastures with cattle access to water bodies	☐	☐	_____
Commercial forestry activities including harvesting and site-preparation	☐	☐	_____
Extensive areas of streambank failure or channel enlargement	☐	☐	_____
Other Agricultural Activities			
Confined animal (cattle or swine) feeding operations and concentrations of animals	☐	☐	_____
Animal waste stabilization ponds	☐	☐	_____
Poultry houses	☐	☐	_____
Highways and Parking Areas			
Shopping Centers and commercial areas	☐	☐	_____
Interstate and controlled access highways and inter-changes	☐	☐	_____
Major highways and arterial streets	☐	☐	_____
Other extensive vehicle parking areas	☐	☐	_____
Mining			
Quarries with sediment basins in live flowing streams	☐	☐	_____
Transportation and Motor Vehicle Services			
Truck cleaning services	☐	☐	_____
Public or private automobile repair facilities	☐	☐	_____
Car washes and large auto dealers	☐	☐	_____
Rail or container transfer yards	☐	☐	_____
Airports with fuel handling/aircraft repair	☐	☐	_____

Businesses and Industry, General	Adjacent to Water	In Watershed	Notes on Location and Frequency of Activity
Activities with exterior storage or exchange of materials	☐	☐	_____
Activities with poor housekeeping practices indicated by stains leading to streams or storm drains or on-site disposal of waste materials	☐	☐	_____
Heavy industries such as textiles and carpet, pulp and paper, metal, and vehicle production or fabrication	☐	☐	_____
Dry cleaners/outside chemical storage	☐	☐	_____

Food and Kindred Products

	Adjacent to Water	In Watershed	
Fertilizer production plants	☐	☐	_____
Feed preparation plants	☐	☐	_____
Meat and poultry slaughtering or processing plants	☐	☐	_____
Construction Materials			_____
Wood Treatment plants	☐	☐	_____
Concrete and asphalt batch plants	☐	☐	_____

Waste Recycling, Movement, and Disposal

	Adjacent to Water	In Watershed	
Junk and auto salvage yards	☐	☐	_____
Solid waste transfer stations	☐	☐	_____
Landfills and dumps	☐	☐	_____
Recycling centers	☐	☐	_____
Drum cleaning sites	☐	☐	_____

Illicit Waste Discharges*

	Adjacent to Water	In Watershed	
Sanitary sewer leaks or failures	☐	☐	_____
Overflowing sanitary sewer manholes due to clogging or hydraulic overload	☐	☐	_____
Bypasses at treatment plants or relief valves in hydraulically overloaded sanitary sewer lines	☐	☐	_____
Domestic or industrial discharges	☐	☐	_____
Extensive areas with aged/malfunctioning septic tanks	☐	☐	_____
Dry weather flows from pipes (with detectable indications of pollution)	☐	☐	_____
Streamside areas of illegal dumping	☐	☐	_____

* If found (most likely during stream surveys), these activities should be immediately reported to the local government or the EPD regional office. These phone numbers are found in Chapter 4 of the Georgia Adopt-A-Stream Manual.

II. General Water Body and Watershed Characteristics (Group 1)

This information will be gathered from your wetland, lake, or stream segment.

1. **Note the number of hydrologic modifications on your water body:** *structures that alter water flow.*

None	_____	Beaver dams	_____
Dams	_____	Dredge spoils	_____
Bridges	_____	Pipes	_____
Waterfalls	_____	Other	_____

2. **Note the approximate length of the stream that is affected by the following:** *if assessing a wetland, lake, or pond, some of the following may also affect your water body.*

Stream culvert	_____feet or	_____miles or	_____% of stream length
Stream straightening	_____	_____	_____%
Concrete streambank/bottom	_____	_____	_____
Dredging/channelization	_____	_____	_____
Riprap/gabion		_____	_____
Cattle crossing	_____#		
Stream crossing (for vehicles)	_____#		

3. **Note extent of vegetative buffer along the banks:** *all the lab groups will be monitoring a minimum of 5 sites, at regular intervals (every 500 ft. in a 1/2 mile section). Find the highest upstream tape marker the last lab group has marked, and note the following. Attach photo.*

#	Width in Feet	Location (Left bank, Right bank, or N, S, E, W side of the wetland or lake)	Characteristics and Comments
1			
2			
3			
4			
5			
6			
7			
8			
9			
10			

4. **Check the categories that best describe the general appearance of the water body:**

Litter:

☐ No litter visible

☐ Small litter occasionally (i.e., cans, paper)

☐ Small litter common

☐ Large litter occasionally (i.e., tires, pallets, shopping carts)

☐ Large litter common

Special Problems:

☐ Spills of chemicals, oils, etc.

☐ Fish kills

☐ Wildlife, waterfowl kills

Erosion:

☐ No bank erosion or areas of erosion very rare; no artificial stabilization

☐ Occasional areas of bank erosion

☐ Areas of bank erosion common

☐ Artificial bank stabilization (i.e., riprap) present

5. **Comments on general water body and watershed characteristics:** (e.g., date and size of fish kill, increased rate of erosion evident, litter most evident after storms)

Fish kills should be immediately reported to the DNR Wildlife Resources Division.

6. **Summarize notable changes that have taken place since last year (if this is not your first year conducting the WatershedSurvey).**

III. Pipe and Drainage Ditch Inventory (Group 1)

In this section, provide information on pipes and drainage ditches found on the banks or in the water body. These pipes/ditches can be abandoned or active. Note the information for each pipe or drainage ditch you observe. *Make additional notes if necessary.*

Pipe #	Location	Type	Size	Flow	Water body Condition	Comments

1. *Number* of each pipe/ditch for mapping/location purposes.

2. *Location* of pipe/ditch: note whether in water, bank, near water body or other. Describe.

3. Identify *type* of pipe (list all that apply): PVC, iron, concrete, galvanized; industrial outfall, sewage treatment plant outfall, storm drain, combined sewer overflow; agricultural field drainage, paddock or feedlot drainage, settlement basin/pool drainage, parking lot drainage, unknown, other

4. *Size*: measure approximate diameter of pipe: inches or centimeters

5. Describe the discharge *flow*: Rate of flow: none, intermittent, trickle, steady, heavy,

    Appearance: clear, foamy, turbid, oily sheen, color, other

    Odor: none, rotten eggs/sewage, chemical, chlorine, other

6. Water body condition: describe the bank/water body below pipe or drain- age ditch: no problem evident, eroded, sewage filter (e.g., toilet paper), litter (e.g., bottles, cans), lots of algae, other.

7. Comments on pipes and drainage ditches

IV. Physical Sampling (Group 2)

Please check with your GLA that test instructions have not changed.

SETTLEABLE SOLIDS AND TURBIDITY

Settleable solids include sediment and other particles that are large enough to settle out of solution. Turbidity levels take into account all particles suspended in the water column, including small colloidal-sized particles, like clay.

1. Collect sample water in a bucket halfway down from the water surface and upstream from where you have been walking. Do not stir up bottom sediments when collecting the sample. Return to shore. Do not allow the sample to settle.

2. Settleable Solids: Slowly fill the Imhoff cone (plastic) with 1 liter of sample water, stir, and allow to settle for 45 minutes. Solids settle to the bottom and are measured as a volume of the total, in millimeters per liter.

3. Turbidity: Slowly pour a new sample of water into the 30-inch plastic tube while looking down vertically into it. When the water level reaches the point at which you can barely see the "X" on the bottom of the tube, stop pouring. Record the water level (in cm) from the scale on the side of the tube. Stir up the sample and repeat. (You'll be averaging two readings from each of 3 different points in the stream.) Convert the average reading from cm to inches and then to NTU, a measure of the amount of light scattered by suspended material in the sample, using the following table.

Inches	NTU		Inches	NTU		Inches	NTU
2.5 to 2.75	240		7.6 to 8.5	40		15.6 to 16.5	15
2.76 to 3.25	185		8.6 to 9.5	35		16.6 to 17.5	14
3.26 to 3.75	150		9.6 to 10.5	30		17.6 to 18.5	13
3.76 to 4.25	120		10.6 to 11.5	27		18.6 to 19.5	12
4.26 to 4.75	100		11.6 to 12.5	24		19.6 to 20.5	11
4.76 to 5.5	90		12.6 to 13.5	21		20.6 to 21.5	10
5.6 to 6.5	65		13.6 to 14.5	19		>21.6	<10
6.6 to 7.5	50		14.6 to 15.5	17			

AIR AND WATER TEMPERATURE

Use the dissolved oxygen meter for water temperature.

DISSOLVED OXYGEN

Turn on the green power button and wait for the meter to show a reading. You will need to have a reading in mg/L (or ppm). Wade out into the water with gloves on, remove the probe by pulling it firmly out of its holder, and CAREFULLY immerse the tip into the water. Note temperature and dissolved oxygen levels at two locations. Rinse the probe with pure distilled water from your bottle BEFORE returning the probe to its holder.

V. Chemical Sampling (Group 3)

Coliscan Easygel Test for Detection of <u>E. coli</u> and Other Fecal Coliform Bacteria

The test requires that Petri plates remain undisturbed for up to an hour.

1. Use a marker to label the edge of a Coliscan dish with your name, lab time, and GLA name.

2. Wearing gloves, collect a water sample from beneath the surface of the stream.

3. Use a sterile pipette and transfer 1 ml of lake/stream water into the Easygel bottle. **Be careful not to touch the inside of the bottle or cap with anything to maintain sterile conditions.**

4. Swirl the bottle to mix, then pour into the labeled Petri dish. Place lids back on dish and gently swirl until the entire dish is covered with liquid. **Be careful not to splash over the side or on the lid.**

5. Place dishes right-side-up on a level spot, preferably warm, until solid.

6. Incubate at 35°C for 24 hours or at room temperature for 48 hours.

7. Inspect the dishes and count the purple colonies (*not* light blue, blue-green, white, or pink). Multiply that number by 100 to determine the number of fecal coliform bacterial colonies per 100 ml of water. Commonly established measures of acceptable fecal coliform levels differ depending on how the water comes into contact with the individual. In the case of waters used for activities such as swimming, where there is primary contact with the water source, fecal coliform counts should be 200 or less per 100 ml water sample. Secondary contact with water, such as with fishing, suggests that fecal coliform counts be 2000 or less per 100 ml sample.

For each of the following tests, try to touch the test strips with your fingers as little as possible.

PH AND ALKALINITY

pH measures the concentration of H+ ions (acid) in the solution. Alkalinity measures the acid neutralizing (buffering) capacity of the water. Dip one test strip into a container with your collected water sample for 10 seconds without any motion. Remove and immediately (within 15 seconds) match pH color and then match total alkalinity color before 30 seconds have elapsed.

NITRATES

Dip one test strip into a container with your collected water sample. Remove the strip and wait one minute for the colors to develop. Match the Nitrate plus Nitrite (end pad) and Nitrite colors. Complete the color matching **within the next 1 minute**.

ORTHOPHOSPHATES

Follow directions given on test strip bottle.

VI. Macroinvertebrate Sampling (Group 4)

Macroinvertebrates can be found in many kinds of habitats—places like riffles (where shallow water flows quickly over rocks), packs of leaves, roots hanging into the water, old wood or logs, or the streambed. The method you choose for collection depends on habitat.

HOW DO I SAMPLE? IT DEPENDS ON THE TYPE OF STREAM BOTTOM.

First determine your type:

Rocky bottom streams have fast moving water with large rocks and boulders and long stretches of smooth water pools. For this habitat two groups will need to collect organisms from both riffle areas and leaf packs using a kick seine. **Wear gloves and boots or waders.**

1. Identify three riffle areas, and collect in a 2 × 2 foot plot in each area using a kick seine. Choose an area where the water is 3 to 12 inches deep. Place the kick seine downstream and firmly wedge the seine into the streambed, weighting the bottom edges with rocks. Gently rub any loose debris off rocks and sticks so that you catch everything in the seine. When you have "washed off" any rocks in a 2 × 2 foot plot, kick the streambed with your feet. Push rocks around; shuffle your feet so that you really kick up the streambed. Now gently lift up the seine, being careful not to lose any of the macroinvertebrates you have caught. Take the seine over to an area where you can wash the contents into a bucket.

2. Now look for decayed (old, dead) packs of leaves next to rocks or logs or on the streambed anywhere throughout a 16 square foot area. Add 4 handfuls (1 square cubic foot each) of decayed leaves to your sample bucket.

Muddy bottom streams have slower flowing water and bottoms composed of fine silt, sand, and coarse gravel. For this habitat, 3 groups will collect organisms in three different locations by scooping a D-Frame (or dip) net with a quick forward motion to sample a square foot area, and then placing the contents into three separate buckets of stream water. **Wear gloves and boots.**

1. **Vegetated margins:** Take 7 scoops from the area of overhanging plants and submerged root mats along the bank of the stream. Move the dip-net quickly in a bottom-to-surface motion (scoop toward the stream bank), jabbing at the bank to loosen organisms. Each scoop of the net should cover one foot of submerged area.

2. **Woody debris with organic matter:** Take 4 scoops from woody debris from living trees, roots, limbs, sticks, leaf packs, cypress knees, and other submerged organic matter. To gather material, approach the area from downstream and hold the net under the section of wood you wish to sample, such as a submerged log. Rub the surface of the log for the total surface area of one square foot. It is also good to dislodge some of the bark as organisms may be hiding underneath. You can also collect sticks, leaf litter, and rub roots attached to submerged logs. Be sure to thoroughly examine any small sticks you collect before discarding them. There may be caddisflies, stoneflies, riffle beetles, and midges attached to the bark.

3. **Sand/rock/gravel:** Take 3 scoops from the coarsest area of streambed where gravel or sand has been deposited (sometimes at a bend in the river). To gather material, move the net forward (upstream) with a jabbing motion to dislodge the first few inches of gravel, sand, or rocks. You may want to gently wash the rocks in the bucket. If you have any large rocks (>2 inches) you should also kick the substrate upstream of the net to dislodge any burrowing organisms. (Remember to disturb only one square foot of upstream sample area.) Each time you sample you should sweep the mesh bottom of the D-frame net back and forth through the water (not allowing water to run over the top of the net) to rinse fine silt from the net.

Some samples are composed almost entirely of fine silt and mud. To separate aquatic organisms, place sample in a bucket with water and stir. Pour off water in D-Frame net and repeat 3 times. Macroinvertebrates will be caught in the net. Before dumping the remaining mud, inspect bucket for snails or mollusks. This process is called elutriation.

GLOSSARY

Animal waste stabilization ponds: In the U.S., stabilization ponds have been in use since 1901. There are about 7,500 stabilization ponds used to treat wastewater and industrial wastes in the country. There are four main types of stabilization ponds, all of which use microorganisms to degrade and detoxify both inorganic and organic constituents: facultative ponds, anaerobic ponds, aerated ponds, and aerobic ponds. The type of organisms used will depend on the kind of wastewater pond. The major function of stabilization ponds is to remove nutrients and other waste by-products from the wastewater. There are often high levels of pathogens present in the stabilization ponds.

Arterial streets: Main roads.

CFU: colony forming units

Channelized: Streams naturally meander; when streams are channelized, the flow is redirected from its natural course, usually into a straighter path.

Colloidal particles: Particulate matter which are dispersed in a continuous medium in a manner that prevents them from being filtered easily or settled rapidly.

Dredging: The removal or displacement of earth including gravel, sand, mud, or silt, and other materials or debris from any body of water and its associated shoreline and wetlands. Dredging is normally done for specific purposes, such as constructing and maintaining canals, navigation channels, harbors, or marinas, sub-marine pipelines, or cable crossings; also for obtaining material for fill or construction; or for dike repair and maintenance. Dredging may also be used for underwater mining activities.

Dredge spoils: Dredge spoil is the material removed by dredging. Dredge spoil disposal is the depositing of dredged materials on land or into water bodies for the purpose of either creating new or additional lands for other uses or disposing of the by-products of dredging.

Gabion: A hollow metal cylinder used especially in constructing dams and foundations.

Gully: A deep ditch or channel cut in the earth by running water after a prolonged downpour.

Hydraulic overload: This is what occurs when the flow in a portion of the sewer system exceeds its hydraulic carrying capacity. Hydraulic is defined as of, involving, moved by, or operated by a fluid, especially water, under pressure.

NTU: Turbidity is measured in Nephelometric *Turbidity* Units or NTU, which represents the average volume scattering over a defined angular range. Both particle size and concentration of suspended solids as well as dissolved solids can affect this reading. When measuring suspended solids, the instruments measure concentration, often in parts per million.

POLLUTION:

- **Point source** comes from industries and sewage treatment plants.
- **Nonpoint source** pollution is added to watersheds as rainfall moving over and through the ground carries along natural (silt, salts, sediments) or human-made pollutants (petroleum products, metals, fertilizers, herbicides, insecticides, bacteria). Sediments, oils, and other pollutants are often carried into watersheds in large amounts during storm runoff that can create erosion due to water running quickly off of impervious surfaces like paved parking lots and

shopping centers. Streams and rivers in areas where greater than 10% of the land is covered with impervious surfaces are impacted by a significant negative stream health impact.

PVC (Poly vinyl chloride): A common thermoplastic resin, used in a wide variety of manufactured products, including rainwear, garden hoses, phonograph records, and floor tiles.

Quarry: An open excavation or pit from which stone is obtained by digging, cutting, or blasting.

Riprap: A loose assemblage of broken stones erected in water or on soft ground as a foundation.

Sediment: Particulate matter that is carried by water or wind and deposited on the surface of the land or the bottom of a body of water.

Snags: Fallen limbs or small log piles.

Stream culvert: A sewer or drain crossing under a road or embankment.

Substrate: An underlying layer. A layer of earth beneath the surface soil; subsoil.

Watershed: The land area from which water, sediment, and dissolved materials drain to a common point along a stream, wetland, lake, or river (Georgia Adopt-a-Stream Resources, Watershed Manual).

GEORGIA ADOPT-A-STREAM

Chemical Data Forms

To be conducted every month

Return to: GA AAS
4220 International Parkway
Suite 101
Atlanta, GA 30354

Use this form and the Adopt-A-Stream methods to record important information about the health of your stream. By keeping accurate and consistent records of your physical/chemical tests, you can document current conditions and changes in water quality.

Investigators: _____ Stream name:

_____Date:

_____Time: _____Picture/Photo Documentation? yes / no

Site/location Description: _____

Rain in the last 24 hours		*Present Conditions*		
☐ heavy rain	☐ steady rain	☐ heavy rain	☐ steady rain	☐ intermittent rain
☐ intermittent rain	☐ none	☐ overcast	☐ partly cloudy	☐ clear/sunny

Amount of rain if known?_____   inches in the last _____ hours/days

BASIC TESTS	**Sample 1**	**Sample 2**	
Air Temperature	_____	_____	(°C)
Water Temperature	_____	_____	(°C)
pH	_____	_____	(1–14)
Dissolved Oxygen	_____	_____	(mg/L or ppm)
Settleable Solids	_____	_____	(ml/L)
ADVANCED TESTS			
Total Alkalinity	_____	_____	(mg/L or ppm)
Nitrate Nitrogen	_____	_____	(mg/L or ppm)
Orthophosphate	_____	_____	(mg/L or ppm)
OTHER TESTS			
Fecal Coliform	_____	_____	(cfu/100 mL)
Turbidity	_____	_____	(NTU)
	_____	_____	
	_____	_____	

Special Lab Analysis: Name of lab performing tests: _____

Comments: _____

Investigators: _____ Stream name: _____

_____Date:

_____Time: _____Picture/Photo Documentation? yes / no

Site/location Description: _____

Rain in the last 24 hours		Present Conditions		
☐ heavy rain	☐ steady rain	☐ heavy rain	☐ steady rain	☐ intermittent rain
☐ intermittent rain	☐ none	☐ overcast	☐ partly cloudy	☐ clear/sunny
Amount of rain if known?_____		inches in the last _____ hours/days		

(check all that apply)

Method used: ☐ Muddy bottom ☐ Rocky bottom

Habitat selected ☐ riffle ☐ leaf pack/woody debris ☐ streambed with silty area (very fine)

for sampling: ☐ streambed with sand/small gravel ☐ vegetated bank ☐ other (specify)

Use letter codes (A = 1–9, B = 10–99, C = 100 or more) to record the numbers of organisms found in the total sample. Then add up the number of letters in each column and multiply by the indicated value. The following columns are divided based on the organism's sensitivity to pollution.

SENSITIVE	SOMEWHAT SENSITIVE	TOLERANT
☐ caddisfly	☐ beetle	☐ aquatic worms
☐ hellgrammite	☐ larvae	☐ blackfly larvae
☐ mayfly	☐ clams	☐ leeches
☐ nymphs	☐ crane fly larvae	☐ midge larvae
☐ gilled snails	☐ crayfish	☐ pouch snails
☐ riffle beetle adult	☐ damselfly nymphs	
☐ stonefly nymphs	☐ scuds	**# of letters times 1 =**
☐ water penny larvae	☐ sowbugs	
	☐ fishfly larvae	
☐**# of letters times 3 =**	☐ alderfly larvae	
	☐**# of letters times 2 =**	

Now add together the three index values = _____total index value

Water Quality Rating: ☐ Excellent (>22) ☐ Good (17–22) ☐ Fair (11–16) ☐ Poor (<11)

The total index value will give you an indication of the water quality of your stream. Good water quality is indicated by a variety of different kinds of organisms, with no one kind making up the majority of the sample.

EVERYBODY OUT OF THE POOL II: STUDENT PRESENTATIONS AND DRAFTING LETTERS

QUESTIONS TO ADDRESS IN YOUR PRESENTATION

You will need to get together with your teammates and prepare a 5-minute presentation of the questions, tests, and conclusions your group made from last week's lab. These presentations will be used by yourself and your peers to compose a letter to a local authority about the health of the water source that you visited and tested for water quality indicators (see the sample letter at the end of this section). For your presentation, be enthusiastic and be prepared to answer questions from your peers. Use the following guidelines (a rubric that is based upon these guidelines can be found in eLC):

Each group member has to say something. It's fine to use a notecard for prompts.

Anything taken from the manual needs to be in your own words and understandable for everyone with no prior knowledge.

- **Context:** Provide information about why officials would want to know this information, including:
    - ○ *Questions:* State the initial questions you hoped to answer from your tests.
    - ○ *Justification:* Include relevant background information about why these tests are done.
    - ○ *Tests:* Explain the normal values/levels/ranges expected for these tests and how the tests were performed.
- **Claims:** What is your claim or conclusion about the water quality of this creek?
- **Evidence:** How do you know? What data and observations from your tests led you to your claim?
- **Explanation:** Explain why you think the water quality is at the level you observed.

What follows is a sample letter that you might write and send to inform a local official about your water quality tests, results, and interpretations. Use this and the associated Water Quality Letter rubric in eLC to help you construct your letter.

SAMPLE LETTER TO INFORM LOCAL OFFICIAL

February 25, 2000
Concerned Citizen
123 Watershed Plaza
Streams, GA 30000

Mayor George Buggs
Rivers City Hall
555 Wetlands Way
Streams, GA 30000

Dear Honorable Mayor Buggs,

I would like to inform you of an interesting and exciting project my neighbors and I are working on. Several of us who live near Ripple Rock Creek decided to learn more about the creek and start protecting it. We have started an Adopt-A-Stream project and registered with the Environmental Protection Division's Georgia Adopt-A-Stream program.

We started the project because we are concerned about the continuing development in our area. Ripple Rock Creek is a beautiful creek and we want to make sure it stays that way. Our Ripple Rock Adoption Project is one way to learn about and protect the creek and share our findings with others.

The Ripple Rock Adoption Project will help protect the creek because we will regularly evaluate water quality, share our results with others, pick up litter, and plant trees to stabilize an eroding streambank. We also know whom to call if a water quality problem is noticed.

Enclosed in this letter is a summary of our initial findings about our stream's water quality. We completed a Watershed Walk and visual survey along with chemical and biological monitoring and our results show the creek is generally in good shape. The land surrounding the creek (the watershed) is generally undeveloped, however, new development upstream concerns us. One upstream builder was polluting the creek with sediment and litter and we are hoping that you will help convince county officials to convince the builder to put up silt fences and to store construction debris away from the creek. We are also concerned that we keep the area next to the creek natural, so that this buffer area will protect the stream from sunlight and higher temperatures and help reduce pollutants that may wash into the creek during a storm.

Watershed Survey: Topographical maps of the area were used to study the watershed before the Walk. During the Walk, we recorded land uses and potential impacts to water quality along a one mile section of the creek. We found that the creek drains both residential and industrial areas. There are some areas that need to be cleaned up and two places where the streambank is eroding. Also, downstream of the residential area lots of algae was noticed in the water, an indication that excessive nutrients are present.

Physical and Chemical Sampling: We were initially concerned about the potential for fertilizer and yard chemicals used in the new development near the stream washing into the water. Visual surveys confirm that there is a noticeable difference in water appearance and presence of algae upstream and downstream of the residential area. However, when we monitored the dissolved oxygen, phosphate, and nitrate levels they were within the acceptable range. We did see a higher than normal level of settleable solids that are consistent with the damage we fear is occurring as a result of the upstream building. In addition, the temperature levels of the stream were higher than the levels that are needed to support aquatic organisms like fish. The removal of trees along the streambed has probably resulted in a lack of the type of tree cover that helps cool the water for fish and other species.

Biological Sampling: The type of organisms we were able to gather from our biological monitoring was the most powerful evidence that we found that the health of the stream was in jeopardy. Many aquatic insects and other organisms that serve as food for fish live in the water for extended periods of time (sometimes a year), so they make excellent indicators of the overall health of a waterbody. Some organisms are more sensitive to environmental conditions while others can tolerate high temperatures and pollution. In our monitoring, we were saddened to find virtually none of the more sensitive organisms such as mayfly and caddisfly nymphs that serve as food for fish. Instead, we found only aquatic worms, leeches, and snails. Overall, our water quality rating based on the macroinvertebrates was poor.

We write to try to convince you that this stream can be restored to the healthy levels that are needed to support life. The overall quality of the water in this stream affects everyone who lives downsteam and everyone that uses water from the river that this stream empties into. We urge you to act to protect our community's resource. May we count on your support?

We look forward to hearing from you.

Sincerely,

Concerned Citizen
Ripple Rock Adoption Project

THE CREATURE FROM BENEATH I:
C. elegans EXPERIMENT

Imagine that you took a scoop of soil from your backyard compost heap and placed it onto a Petri dish. You would be amazed at what could crawl out, like the 1 mm little guys shown in the picture below. They are harmless roundworms, a type of nematode of the species *Caenorhabditis elegans*, or *C. elegans*. Grown in a lab on Petri dishes, this photo shows them crawling through a lawn of their favorite food, *E. coli* bacteria. Developed as a genetic model organism by Sydney Brenner in the 1970s,

C. elegans has been instrumental in uncovering the secrets of some of the most basic cellular processes in animals. Research on embryonic development, sex determination, aging, and alcoholism has benefited from the studies of *C. elegans*.

BACKGROUND INFORMATION

Adult *C. elegans* are usually **hermaphrodites**—meaning they make both eggs and sperm. **They can reproduce by self-fertilization OR by mating with a male. Males have to mate with a hermaphrodite to reproduce. Two hermaphrodites cannot mate with each other.**

Table 8.1. Characteristics of chromosomes.

Organism	Somatic Cells (all other cells that are NOT germ/sex cells)	Germ/Sex Cells (sperm/egg)
Chromosome number		
Humans	46 (23 pairs)	23
C. elegans	12 (6 pairs)	6
Number of autosomes		
Humans	44 (22 pairs)	22
C. elegans	10 (5 pairs)	5
Types of sex chromosomes		
Humans	2: X and Y	1: either X or Y
C. elegans	1: X	1: either X or none (O)

INSIDE THE NUCLEI OF SOMATIC CELLS:

Human: 22 pairs autosomes + XX in females, 22 pairs autosomes + XY in males

C. elegans: 5 pairs autosomes + XX in hermaphrodites, 5 pairs autosomes + XO in males

INSIDE THE NUCLEI OF GERM/SEX CELLS:

Human: Females produce eggs that have nuclei with 22 autosomes + X. Males produce sperm that have nuclei with 22 autosomes + X **OR** 22 autosomes + Y.

C. elegans: Hermaphrodites produce eggs that have nuclei with 5 autosomes + X. Hermaphrodites produce sperm that have nuclei with 5 autosomes + X. Males produce sperm that have nuclei with 5 autosomes + X **OR** 5 autosomes + O.

PRE-LAB 8: THE CREATURE FROM BENEATH I

Note: All pre-lab assignments are due the day noted in the syllabus and are NOT subject to the 10%/day for late work policy as stated in the syllabus. You will not receive any credit for parts of this assignment that are incomplete or not attempted.

Instructions: Use the following information to answer Questions 1–5.

Common Nomenclature

Homozygous = AA/aa

Heterozygous = Aa

sma-2 = small (small size phenotype)

+ = wild type (normal phenotype)

Genotype = combination of alleles

Phenotype = physical appearance

Assume that the traits described are **autosomal** (not on the X chromosome).

You will need to use Punnett squares to answer most of the questions.

1. For each of the following *C. elegans* parents placed onto a seeded Petri dish, predict what percent of the 100 or so offspring would be male or hermaphrodite. **(1.5 points)**

		Parents		
		1 hermaphrodite	**1 male**	**1 male plus 1 hermaphrodite**
Predicted Offspring:	**% hermaphrodite**			
	% male			

MONOHYBRID CROSSES:

Crosses in which one pair of alleles is involved.

2. *C. elegans* with the mutation **sma-2** results in a mutant phenotype characterized by small body size. You place a hermaphrodite that is homozygous for **sma-2** and a hermaphrodite that is homozygous wild-type (+) on a single plate.

    a. Predict the **phenotypic and genotypic ratios** of the F1 offspring from these two hermaphrodites. **(1 point)**

    b. How can you determine if this **F1** generation came from self-fertilization or cross-fertilization? **(1 point)**

For questions 3–5, **you** must choose if the mutation is dominant or recessive.

3. You place a **sma-2** homozygous hermaphrodite and a **wild-type** (+) homozygous male on a Petri dish. Assume an **F1** cross takes place.

    Draw the Punnett square for this **F1** cross. Use the symbol + for the wild-type allele and **sma-2** for the mutant allele. **(0.5 points)**

    List the phenotypic and genotypic ratios if **sma-2** is dominant. **(0.5 points)**

    List the phenotypic and genotypic ratios if **sma-2** is recessive. **(0.5 points)**

4. A heterozygous **F1** hermaphrodite offspring from the successful mating between a *sma-2* homozygous hermaphrodite and a wild-type (+) homozygous male (cross in Question 3) is placed on a new plate.

   Draw the Punnett square for an **F2** cross of this **F1** hermaphrodite offspring if it self-fertilizes for this cross. Use the symbol + for the wild-type allele and *sma-2* for the mutant allele. **(0.5 points)**

   List the phenotypic and genotypic ratios if *sma-2* is dominant. **(0.5 points)**

   List the phenotypic and genotypic ratios if *sma-2* is recessive. **(0.5 points)**

5. You place a *sma-2* homozygous hermaphrodite and a **wild-type** (+) homozygous male on a Petri dish, but the male dies before fertilizing the hermaphrodite.

   Draw the Punnett square for this **F1** cross. Use the symbol + for the wild-type allele and *sma-2* for the mutant allele. **(0.5 points)**

List the phenotypic and genotypic ratios if **sma-2** is dominant. **(0.5 points)**

List the phenotypic and genotypic ratios if **sma-2** is recessive. **(0.5 points)**

THE CREATURE FROM BENEATH I EXPERIMENT

Objective: Over the next three weeks, determine the pattern of inheritance for your *C. elegans* mutation of choice.

- Is the mutation dominant, recessive, or incomplete dominance?
- Is the mutation autosomal or sex-linked?

Background

You have access to three different mutant *C. elegans* as well as the wild-type. Here are pictures of all four strains:

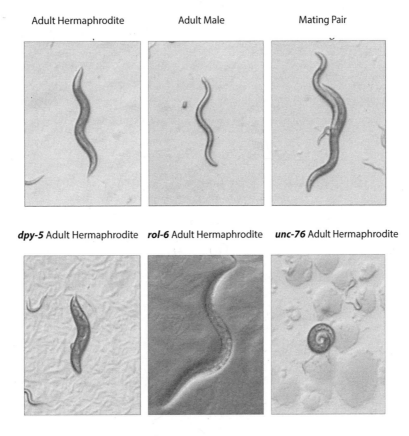

©Sinclair Stammers / Science Source

"Like a Virgin": Identifying Different Developmental Stages of *C. elegans*

In order to set up crosses, you need to distinguish between adult and juvenile stages of the hermaphrodites as well as between males and hermaphrodites. In general, hermaphrodites in the larval stage that will be most likely to mate (L4 stage) will have a smoothly tapered tail and a distinguishing white oval with a small black dot in the middle of the animal that will develop into the vulva (structure used to lay eggs). Males can be identified by a bump/hook at the end of their tails.

"NOBODY LIKES ME, EVERYBODY HATES ME,
GUESS I'LL GO EAT WORMS,

LONG, THIN, SLIMY ONES; SHORT, FAT, JUICY ONES,
ITSY, BITSY, FUZZY WUZZY WORMS."

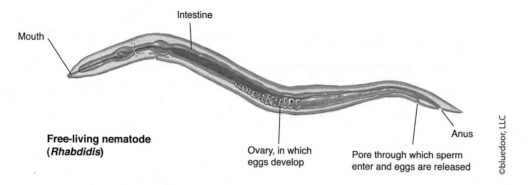

Mouth   Intestine   Anus

Free-living nematode
(*Rhabdidis*)

Ovary, in which eggs develop

Pore through which sperm enter and eggs are released

©bluedoor, LLC

Please read the "Available Tools and Equipment" AND "Ideas to Consider" sections below. Then in your group, determine a plan to carry out your experiment. Fill out the Experimental Design Section and show it to your GLA BEFORE you begin.

Available Tools and Equipment

- Seeded Petri dishes: 2 per group
- Worm "spatulas"
- Dissecting microscopes
- *C. elegans* mutants (three) that are homozygous for the mutations: only hermaphrodites available (NO males)
- Wild-type, homozygous *C. elegans* (males and hermaphrodites)

Ideas to Consider

You will need to know the answers to these in order to accomplish the Objective.

- You place a single, **mutant** virgin hermaphrodite (L4 stage or younger) on a seeded Petri dish. What is the expected phenotype and sex of the offspring?

- You place a single, **wild-type** virgin hermaphrodite (L4 stage or younger) on a seeded Petri dish. What is the expected phenotype and sex of the offspring?

- You place a single, **mutant** L4 hermaphrodite with a wild-type male on a seeded Petri dish. What is the expected phenotype and sex of the offspring?

- Why would you want to cross your **mutant hermaphrodite with a wild-type** male instead of just allowing the mutant hermaphrodite to self-fertilize?

- How many worms (# hermaphrodites and # males) should be placed on each plate? For example, would it be better to have several males and one hermaphrodite or several hermaphrodites and one male?

- Do you expect a 100% successful mating each time? Why or why not?

LAB 8: OBSERVATIONS OF *C. elegans*

Experimental Design

Using a dissecting microscope, place a Petri dish that contains wild-type *C. elegans* (mixture of hermaphrodites and males) onto the microscope stage. Your GLA will help you with the microscope as well as identification of eggs, larvae, adult hermaphrodites, and males. Make a list of the distinguishing characteristics of the wild-type homozygous males and hermaphrodites. You should list both physical and behavioral characteristics that distinguish these two groups of organisms. **(1 point)**

	Sex Chromosomes	Distinguishing Physical and Behavioral Characteristics
Hermaphrodites	XX	
Males	XO	

- Observe the **mutant C. elegans** assigned to your lab bench. Similar to the table above, describe distinguishing physical and behavioral characteristics of the worms. Remember, the worms are homozygous and all are hermaphrodites.

Mutant Name	Distinguishing Physical and Behavioral Characteristics

- **Objective:** What are your experiments designed to find? **(0.5 points)**

LABORATORY 9

CREATURE FROM BENEATH II:
C. elegans EXPERIMENT

Note: All pre-lab assignments are due the day noted in the syllabus and are NOT subject to the 10%/day for late work policy as stated in the syllabus. You will not receive any credit for parts of this assignment that are incomplete or not attempted.

PRE-LAB 9: CREATURE FROM BENEATH II

Instructions: Use Punnett squares to answer the following questions.

1. There is a mutant *C. elegans* that has a long and thin phenotype. This mutation is called *lon-2*.

   a. When a *lon-2* **hermaphrodite** is crossed with a **wild-type male**, the characteristics of the **F1** offspring are as follows:

   Phenotypes: All males are long and thin, all hermaphrodites are wild-type

   Gender: 50% males, 50% hermaphrodite

   Explain why this occurred: **(1 point)**

   b. What are the expected phenotypic ratios of the **F1** offspring when a *lon-2* **hermaphrodite** undergoes self-fertilization? **(1 point)**

   c. What are the expected phenotypic ratios of the **F1** offspring when a *lon-2* **male** is crossed to a **wild-type homozygous hermaphrodite**? **(1 point)**

Incompletely Dominant Alleles
(Assume Mutations are Autosomal for this Problem):

An intermediate inheritance in which heterozygous alleles are both expressed, resulting in a combined phenotype.

2. Boxer dogs that are brown with black stripes are referred to as *brindle*. The *brindle* gene shows incomplete dominance. The number and darkness of the stripes in *brindle* boxers is highly variable. Some have so many stripes they look almost black. Some have a medium number of stripes. Others have just a few stripes.

    Let gene B = stripes: BB = lots of stripes, Bb = medium stripes, bb = few stripes

    a. You breed a *brindle* that has a lot of stripes with another *brindle* that has only a few stripes. What is the phenotype of their litter of puppies (**F1** offspring)? **(0.5 points)**

    b. You breed two puppies from the **F1** generation in Part a of this question. What is the expected phenotypic ratio of these puppies? **(0.5 points)**

THE CREATURE FROM BENEATH II EXPERIMENT

Objective: Continued from Lab 8 Objective—determine the pattern of inheritance for your *C. elegans* mutation of choice.

- Is the mutation dominant, recessive, or incomplete dominance?
- Is the mutation autosomal or sex-linked?

Background

This week you will observe an **F1** generation that is a result of a cross between a wild-type homozygous male and a wild-type homozygous hermaphrodite mutant that was assigned to your lab bench. You will be instructed to record results of this cross and to make an initial set of conclusions about the pattern of inheritance of the mutant allele you are studying. After these initial conclusions of Plate 1, you will set up a new cross that will produce an **F2** generation.

Available Tools and Equipment

- Petri dish with **F1** generation of homozygous wild-type male and homozygous mutant hermaphrodite
- Freezer blocks
- Seeded Petri dishes: 1 per student
- Worm "spatulas"
- Dissecting microscopes
- Wild-type *C. elegans* (males and hermaphrodites)

Ideas to Consider

You will need to know the answers to these in order to accomplish the objective of the lab.

- There are several worms on your plate which are moving around too fast for you to count. Use the provided freezer blocks to slow your worms down by placing the plates on top of them for 5 minutes BEFORE you start counting worms.
- Use the provided Sharpie pens to create four equal quadrants on the bottom of your plate. Each group member should count and identify the worms in one quadrant.

- Which worms to count: You only want to count worms of which you are absolutely sure of the phenotype and gender.

- How many to count: You need to count at least 100 worms. If you do not have 100 worms to count, we encourage you to collaborate with a group that did the same cross as you so that you can combine worm numbers to reach at least 100.

HOW TO RECORD YOUR EXPERIMENTAL RESULTS:

After one week your plates should have many worms as depicted in the previous figure. Use your predictions from last week, including Punnett squares, to tabulate the numbers of offspring that you observe this week on your plates. If you are unsure of the phenotypes, refer back to the available demonstration plates of the known mutants. You can use a pen to mark the bottom of your plate into quadrants, and then each team member can count a quadrant.

Observations of the Last Week's Plates/Experimental Design

INITIAL OBSERVATIONS AND CONCLUSIONS:

PLATE 1 (1.5 POINTS)

Provide a physical and behavioral description of the observed F_1 offspring. Include counts of males and hermaphrodites.

How do these counts compare with your original prediction?

Do you wish to revise your original hypothesis about the inheritance of the mutation? If so, explain how and why.

This week you will have the opportunity to continue experiments to uncover more about the mutation you chose last week.

- Each student will have one plate available to set up matings to better understand their mutant allele and its pattern of inheritance.

METHOD

Care and Feeding of Your Mutant and Moving your Worms Around

You will be using little **worm "spatulas"** to move the worms around under the microscope. These are slender pieces of platinum wire that are fragile and can bend easily. Always store spatulas upright in the holder provided. You will use alcohol lamps to flame-sterilize your spatulas. Keep your hair tied back, and keep other flammable objects away from the alcohol lamps.

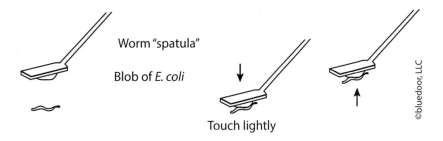

How to move the worms around from the dish with the parents to a fresh dish (for your crosses):

- Sterilize your worm spatula by briefly passing it through the flame of the alcohol lamp and then cool it completely by waiting for 10–15 seconds.
- Dab your worm spatula on the edge of the *E. coli* from the fresh Petri dish such that there is a little blob of bacteria on the bottom of the spatula. Refer to the picture above.
- *Using the dissecting microscope,* touch the bacteria onto the surface of a worm from the parent dish. Gently lift the worm up and place it onto the agar of the fresh dish. Watch as it crawls off, making sure you only transferred one worm.

Some tips:

- Be careful not to poke holes in the agar; the worms can burrow down and escape from the surface, making them impossible to observe or manipulate.
- Be careful that you don't inadvertently transfer eggs or larvae over to your mating plates.
- When using the pick, steady your hand by resting its edge on a flat surface.

Safety Note: In the laboratory, *C. elegans* are grown on agar plates spread with a lawn of *E. coli* bacteria and then incubated at temperatures between 15–25°C. To keep molds and wild bacteria from taking over the plates, aseptic (sterile) technique should always be used when transferring worms. Keep your plates covered as much as possible, and make sure not to touch the surface of the plate with anything that is not sterile. Although the strain of *E. coli* used in this experiment is not normally harmful, be sure to disinfect your hands after touching the plates. When you are finished with them, bacterial plates should NOT be thrown into the trash. Please place all *C. elegans* plates back in the plastic storage boxes provided.

PLATE 2 (YOUR PLATE)

Description of parent(s) of this cross: **(0.5 points)**

Why did you choose this cross to help you better understand the pattern of inheritance of your mutant allele? **(1 point)**

- Give the predicted phenotypes and genotypes (autosomal and sex-linked), including ratios of **F2** offspring. Use Punnett squares to help with the predictions. **(1.5 points)**

  - If the mutation is dominant:

  - If the mutation is recessive:

  - If the mutation shows incomplete dominance:

CREATURE FROM BENEATH III:
C. elegans EXPERIMENT

Objective: Continued from Lab 8 Objective—determine the pattern of inheritance for your *C. elegans* mutation of choice.

- Is the mutation dominant, recessive, or incomplete dominance?
- Is the mutation autosomal or sex-linked?

RECORD YOUR EXPERIMENTAL RESULTS

Use your predictions from last week, including Punnett squares, to tabulate the numbers of offspring that you observe this week on your plates.

Observations of the Mystery Mutant Plates

PLATE 2 (YOUR PLATE)

Provide a physical and behavioral description of the observed **F2** offspring. Include counts of males and hermaphrodites.

How does this compare with your original prediction?

Do you wish to revise your original hypothesis about the inheritance of the mutation? If so, explain how and why.